AFFECTIVE SAFETY MANAGEMENT

BY DR. TIM MARSH

"the next step in safety leadership"

Paul Hopkin, Hon Vice President IIRSM

Dedication

For Lauren, Georgie and Lewis. Still at an age when they all assume this is the best book ever written and where getting the balance between protection and independence is a daily battle. It is also dedicated to my partner Debbie – our operations director with special responsibility for safety. If all companies were as safety conscious as she is this book would be pointless.

It is also respectfully dedicated to my friend Ian Whittingham MBE who sadly died just after this book was first published. Ian was a real hero who, following a horrendous accident, dedicated his life selflessly to preventing others suffering his fate. In large part the illness that killed him was caused by him working too hard and not looking after himself as well as he should. He literally lived and died spreading the safety message. He is badly missed by all who knew him.

Acknowledgement

I am enormously grateful to Paul Hopkin and Neil Budworth whose constructive comments and suggestions were hugely helpful. Now as Honorary Vice-President and immediate past President (respectively) of the two largest occupational safety organizations in the UK you'd expect that of course! But it is very much appreciated that they selflessly took the time and were encouraging and supportive too!

Tim Marsh, July 2009

CHAIRMAN'S INTRODUCTION

IIRSM has pioneered the concept of Affective Safety Management (ASM) since its inception by Lyndon Shearman and has continued to move this forward with the help of Dr Tim Marsh of Ryder Marsh Ltd.

With the help of Tim, the IIRSM have now held 3 workshops in Stirling, Manchester and London. Additionally we have held a large ASM Conference in Birmingham which received an overwhelming response and positive feedback.

From mid 2008 Dr Tim Marsh wrote the "Affective Safety Management" handbook for IIRSM and since then we have sold out 3 print-runs and embarked on producing a revised edition.

Therefore, as IIRSM Chairman, I am pleased to endorse the latest version of the ASM handbook and trust that the style and accessibility of the content will provide an enjoyable and enlightening experience.

Keith Scott, IIRSM Chairman

Group Head of Safety, Royal Mail Group

PREFACE

Before the Health and Safety at Work Act 1974, health and safety at work was all about machinery guarding and not much else. When other topics were considered, guards and barriers were considered to be the answer. That changed in 1974 and the new priority became "Safe Systems of Work". It was considered that guards or barriers together with safe systems of work were the total answer to issues associated with health and safety at work.

It soon became obvious that more was required and attention shifted to the avoidance of unsafe acts. Now the approach was three pronged – guards, systems of work and the avoidance of unsafe acts would be sufficient to solve all safety problems. Then came the realisation that unsafe acts could only be avoided if there was a strong safety culture in the organisation. However, this was still not enough, because people need to have more than just safe plant / equipment, together with rules, supervision and encouragement.

The additional need is for an approach that appeals to the emotional as well as the intellectual intelligence of people. It is not enough (for example) to make cars safer, introduce traffic calming devices, seek to eliminate unsafe driving and develop a culture of road safety. Individual drivers need to be engaged on an emotional level. There is a need to win the hearts as well as the minds of drivers. This analysis applies equally well to all work activities.

There is a need for a fifth step in the development of successful safety leadership. This fifth step should be based on the application of emotional intelligence, neurolinguistic programming and other related approaches to the management of safety. IIRSM calls this approach "Affective Safety Management" or ASM. Every ten years or so since 1974 has seen the next development in safety management. Now IIRSM puts forward ASM as the next step in the evolution of successful safety leadership and management.

Paul Hopkin

Hon Vice President IIRSM, July 2008

INTRODUCTION

The author frequently worked with one of the UK's leading safety campaigners – the inimitable Ian Whittingham MBE who very sadly died in May 2009. Ian was paralysed in an accident in Liverpool in 1990 and gives a blistering, passionate and witty talk that never failed to move and inspire. However, there are two specific points that he made that underpin the motivation for writing this book and for all the work that I do. He pointed out that in the same time scale many more UK citizens have been killed working in his industry alone (construction) than have been killed in the battlefields of Afghanistan and Iraq combined. With no offence to UK soldiers intended, somewhat ironically, you only need one nurse or teacher to be killed in their line of work and the newspapers will start a national campaign. He asks "Where are the newspaper campaigns to save all these fathers, sons, mothers and daughters who aren't teachers or nurses? Where is the national campaign for my colleagues? …and that we haven't even begun to talk about deaths because of occupational illness…"

The second point he made is that when he was first in hospital he learned to hate Fridays because Friday was new intake day. He explained how he and his fellow patients would try to keep away from the distraught and devastated families of the new patients because it would remind them of what their own families had been through. His challenge to the audience was "so who will be going in next Friday?" and he pointed out that, quite, we don't know yet we just know that all the beds will be full and that the people who will fill them are walking about as we speak, working, shopping, playing football with their children, riding their bikes…. Now we know we can't close the hospital – but we can make the ward a little less busy.

I've tried to make this book reasonably light-hearted so that it is readable and 'affective' but I try never to forget that a poor safety culture means people killed and maimed – and mourned by their children, partner and parents. In my perfect world we all get to enjoy rambling and golf in our 70s and die of old age in our 80s (in my case of a quick heart attack whilst cheering Wales on to another Grand Slam!) Surely that's not an unreasonable thing to aim for is it?

The concept of "Affective Safety Management" then is a simple combination of several areas of research and best practise methodology. Firstly, it's based on the basic principles of what some call "visible safety leadership". This stresses that managers need to get out on the shop floor and visibly demonstrate their commitment to safety by making the time to go out and observe and discuss.

Safety issues on a regular basis. They need to model safety at all times themselves and challenge all risk that they see – not just the big stuff. The book seeks to explain the psychology behind why this is so important and also has a practical 'things that go wrong with this' troubleshooting section.

Secondly, it draws on the basic principle of behavioural safety. That it's day-to-day behaviours that define a safety culture and that if we look after the little things the bigger things will look after themselves. The book constantly seeks to describe the key day-to-day behaviours that drive a pro-active and improving safety culture. Obviously, we're assuming here that the basic building blocks of safety are in place - risk assessments, training, inductions, safety management systems and the like. What we absolutely do not assume however is that these are comprehensive, user-friendly and both widely understood and applied by the workforce.

Thirdly, and wholly congruent with Reason's 'Just Culture' model, Affective Safety Management is based on the belief that more often than not the individual who has taken or caused a risk will have a reason for what they are doing that is more complex than 'they couldn't be bothered'. Any safety leader, we feel strongly, needs at the very least to understand the principles of 'five whys' analysis and the ABC.

(Antecedents, behaviours and consequences) model of behavioural prediction. So often, when we step back and analyse objectively we find that if we were in their shoes we'd probably have taken the risk too and the book covers questioning techniques that maximise analysis whilst minimising defensiveness.

Lastly, it draws on the field of psychology as practised by the likes of advertising agencies, politicians and TV's Derren Brown. Obviously, one element of this is to use the most effective and interesting training techniques and exercises we can find but it's also about leadership. Leading from the front and insisting on high levels of safety is always going to be key of course but how do you energise and motivate a workforce to follow you with a genuine commitment to world class safety performance? How do you walk away from a person leaving them wanting to act safely for reasons more positive than blind fear of losing their job? The book suggests techniques a little more upbeat and subtle than shouting "Oi! ... YOU... YOU TOTAL IDIOT !!! ... GET ... OVER .... HERE... AND ... GET... OVER ... HERE ... NOOOOWWWWW!"

You could summarise this as:

- Get out there and lead from the front… (because)
- Any risk is too much risk as it mounts up quickly … (so)
- Focus on and challenge day to day issues as well as the 'big' stuff … (by)
- Asking the right questions in the right way… (so that you can)
- Always analyse intelligently before you act… (and when you act remember)
- The best coaches only lose their temper and throw things very occasionally…

I very much hope that at the very least you find some ideas and suggestions useful. In the spirit of learning we know many of you have decades of experience in these matters and we'd really value your constructive comments and criticisms as well as any anecdotes and case studies that you feel might enhance the text. The plan is to produce an updated version in a few years. Please contribute!

CONTENTS

As an Honorary Fellow of the IIRSM I am personally delighted to endorse this book on Affective Safety Management. The International Institute of Risk and Safety Management has correctly identified the importance of attitude and behaviour as key components in the successful management of health and safety at work.

The emphasis in this book on staff involvement, communication and training is entirely consistent with the findings of HSE review of safety culture and safety climate literature in 2005. The HSE report emphasised that leadership, involvement, learning, accountability and communication are key to employee motivation and this book provides practical guidance on how to achieve these important features in safety culture.

I wish the IIRSM every success in this initiative and look forward to further developments related to Affective Safety Management.

Geoffrey Podger

Chief Executive

As minister responsible for health and safety, I am always pleased when a new high profile initiative comes along. The approach to the successful management of health and safety at work represented by Affective Safety Management consolidates and advances existing ideas related to safety learning and motivation.

Initiatives that bring clarity to the role of individuals are always welcome. Attitudes to health and safety and the behaviours that result are very important to the successful management of health and safety at work.

The International Institute of Risk and Safety Management has captured the features of best practice in their Affective Safety Management approach. I look forward to receiving reports on the progress of this initiative and the experience of IIRSM members in implementing ASM.

Lord McKenzie of Luton

Parliamentary Under-Secretary of State (Lords)
Department of Work and Pensions
Minister for Health and Safety

A SELECTION OF COMMENTS ABOUT THE ASM LAUNCH CONFERENCE HELD AT THE BOTANICAL GARDENS, BIRMINGHAM, MAY 2008.

Inspirational, well done! ... (S.A.)

It explained a complex subject in a straight forward way ... (G.I.)

Positive, different and thought provoking ... (B.P.)

Not only informative but lots of fun ... (D.G.)

Excellent, thought provoking and engaging ... demands your attention and moves you to action ... (D.S.)

Well presented, informative and provided an insight to that crucial edge often missing in safety Management ... (M.G.)

Practical, down to earth, interactive and I learnt new techniques ... (K.B.)

The speaker was excellent, wish he worked for us ... (C.S.)

Extremely motivational, Tim's methods of training are interesting... (M.M.)

Witty and sincere ... (A.R.)

A great mixture of fun & seriousness ... got the point across! ... (P.B.)

Excellent speaker ... very entertaining ... (P.S.)

AND A COMMENT ABOUT THE BOOK ...

"I just wanted to let you know how informative and entertaining I found the book. You've incorporated a lot of useful information in an easy to read format that often had me chuckling (usually as I recognized myself and my colleagues...!)" (J.M.)

THEORY OF AFFECTIVE SAFETY MANAGEMENT

CHAPTER 1

SAFETY LEADERSHIP AND LEARNING

Before we cover a little theory and for contextual reasons I'd like to set the tone by starting this book with two case studies. The first about a company that cut accidents to a sixth of previous levels across a dozen sites and the second about a time when I needed some leadership and didn't get it

Management Commitment and Leadership – A Case Study

Some years ago an operations manager and his CEO travelled to the West Country to attend the funeral of an employee who had died whilst working at one of their sites. Now accidents in this company were frequent as the work was very hard and intensive but they found the experience of actually burying someone deeply upsetting and held a meeting at a motorway service station on the way back to head office. The result of that discussion was a very basic mission statement:

"*This bloody well doesn't ever happen again*".

As well as insisting that all site managers attend safety management courses, the company introduced a rule that no one was to be promoted until they had passed their NEBOSH certificate and also brought in some consultants to implement a full behavioural approach to safety across the country. All of this was met with local opposition of course – and the psychology behind why this is inevitable is described in chapter six – but this opposition was simply not tolerated. It was obvious from the start that management "really meant it" and they were able to cut accident rates to a sixth of original levels nationwide over a three year period.

I was the lead consultant on the behavioural element of the project and recall talking to my partner the night after the project commenced and commenting "It's a very rough and ready workplace but I'm sure the senior management are going to make this work. There's something about the look in their eyes that convinces me I'd not like to be in the shoes of the manager who tries to push back against this!"

Tony Blair and Leadership – Where Were You When I Needed You? I was canvassed by some door-stepping Labour counsellors some years ago about the next election and I commented that I was unhappy with recent events. "Ah, Iraq again I expect!... we know" said one but I said that was a separate matter – it was the MMR vaccination jab controversy that was bothering me. More recently the research that linked it to autism has been discredited with large scale international research but it was a real concern at the time and the debate was absolutely raging. In my household the debate about our new born twins raged too. At one point my partner refused to speak to me for a day because I'd suggested it was logical to vaccinate them one at a time in case one reacted badly.

Some weeks before we had to make our decision Tony Blair had flatly refused to confirm or deny if he had allowed his new son to be given the MMR vaccine despite the (perfectly correct as it happens in hindsight) stated government position that it was safe. He surely had access to the best medical advice and it's safe to assume he'd have said so had he followed this advice. I can't express how reassuring it would have been for us at the time if he'd stood up and said 'I've been personally assured it's safe and can confirm we ourselves gave it to Leo just last week ...'. (Since the first edition of the book came out Cherrie Blair has said publicly that they did give their son the vaccine ... I thought at first I'd need to amend this bit. Then I thought even if that's true I think it actually makes it worse!).

These events were hot on the heels of listening to a really great speech that (despite a typical cynicism regarding all politicians) had me thinking 'I'm impressed! Maybe this chap is different". My point is that words can certainly raise your hopes and inspire – and we cover some tips on how to do this in the last section of the book - but real leadership is about behaviour.

Safety Leadership

The Leading Health and Safety at Work document published by the Institute of Directors and the Health and Safety Commission defines safety leadership as:

Strong and active leadership from the top:

- Visible active commitment from the board
- Establishing, effective, downward communication systems and management structures
- Integration of good H&S management with business decisions

Worker involvement:

- Engaging the workforce
- Effective 'upward' communication
- Provide high quality training

Assessing and review

- Identifying and managing health and safety risks

- Accessing (and following) competent advice

- Monitoring, reporting and reviewing performance

As well as covering key issues such as policy, strategy and designated responsibility, it suggests some areas of good practice that I'd like to highlight. Under 'deliver' it suggests "leadership is more effective if visible – board members can re-enforce H&S policy by being seen on the shop floor, following all safety measures themselves and ... be trained in H&S themselves ... and support worker involvement in health and safety". Under 'monitor' it also suggests that involving the workforce in monitoring safety performance can help motivation.

In part the aim of this book is to focus on the 'hands on' element of these guidelines, describe the psychology behind them and to explore in detail what these day to day 'good practice' behaviours look like.

Touring the Shop Floor

Perhaps the first rule of safety leadership approaches such as Affective Safety Management is that managers must get out and about and observe their workers. These processes might be known as 'safety contacts' or 'visible felt leadership' but the basic principle is the same. It is that managers need to visit the shop floor to observe safety themselves and to discuss safety issues with the workers they encounter there. There are two reasons for this – the first is that they might learn something (as discussed in detail in later chapters) and the second because of the symbolism.

Learning by Listening

You may have heard of the 'Bay of Pigs' fiasco, which was the horribly ill conceived and botched invasion of Cuba by the US back in the 1960s. Analysing what went wrong, writers came up with the expression "group think" to describe how even an intelligent and experienced group could sleepwalk into a bad decision. A recent management best-seller, "The Wisdom of Crowds", has covered similar territory.

Teams should follow three basic rules when solving problems:

- Make sure everyone contributes in turn

- Listen carefully, then consider their input objectively

- Even if their contribution is useless, don't laugh or otherwise discourage them from having another go.

The basic premise is quite simply that as the old saying goes 'two heads are better than one' and that the smartest/ most confident/ most experienced/ most senior person in the room can't have all the answers all of the time. More than that, of course, if the discussion is about the practicalities of implementing a safety plan or following a safety rule the person who actually does the job is the expert. A field of research called 'participatory ergonomics' stresses that the person who will use the tool or machinery should be fully consulted and involved in the design stage. It's remarkable how many companies still don't do this as a matter of course.

Symbolism

You may be aware of the expression "what gets measured gets done" and that people will tend to do what they think management wants them to do ... so, if they are taking the trouble to measure it, it must be important to them and since they're the boss...

Research has shown that life is more complex than this. You may also be aware of the study that shows people are less likely to cheat by not dropping coins into an honesty box for example if there is a photo of a person 'staring' at them. The presence of a mirror also reduces cheating – you can 'see' yourself taking advantage and this effect is magnified by wearing a name tag. In short you become less 'invisible' and more likely to think about what you're doing.

Now clearly, this suggests that a workforce will be safer if all workers are in overalls with name tags and surrounded by mirrors... but assuming the cost and the 'hall of mirrors' side effects make this impractical it does explain why visible leadership can be so effective. You're not just a pair of eyes in a photo you're their boss and you're out there in person. Ideally you'll be acting as a 'mirror' too and skilfully encouraging the person to consider their actions.

We will cover several ways of encouraging people to reflect on their actions later in the book.

Why Focus on Safety? (Basketball anyone?)

Because of time pressures, some conscientious managers will include safety as a part of their daily or weekly walkabout. This isn't much of a problem if they genuinely value safety as highly as productivity and for them safety issues are as attention grabbing as productivity issues. This isn't normally the case however ...

Many people have now seen the now famous basketball scene in which an audience is invited to count the passes between the players in yellow where there are half a dozen players, some in yellow and some in blue, mingling and throwing two basketballs about ... it's a surprisingly hard task to do accurately but not as surprising as being told afterwards that a gorilla walked through the middle of the action. About 75% of people fail to spot the gorilla at all and you'll often have someone swear blind that it must be a different clip when it's played back. (If you've not seen this clip e-mail me and I'll send it to you).

The gorilla represents safety, and the passes productivity, and it makes the point that even the largest and most important of issues can be missed if you're not looking out for them: the audience do better when the task is to "count the number of large dangerous animals in this clip"!

Research has also shown, however, that if we are distracted – or just tired – we are far more likely to make mistakes than if we are attentive. (This you knew already of course!) In the world of sales, people who know about this research will try and get hold of you just after morning coffee break if they have a strong pitch and just after lunch if they have a weak one!

What this means in practise is that even if we do spot the gorilla in our midst the conversation might go something like this:

"Was that a gorilla?"

"Ah, yes boss it was ... but it's been fully inducted and we're keeping a close eye on it!"

"Oh ... well I suppose that's OK then.... now about this order that's been delayed..."

This is followed by sitting bolt upright in bed later that night and shouting "oh hell, there's a bloody gorilla loose at work!"

Now if you're a safety professional you'll most probably see the gorillas and the risk associated with them – it's your primary task to look for them – but as everyone knows the strongest safety cultures are driven by line management. They need to make the time to go and look actively for safety issues without distraction.

Communicate with All

The offshore installation manager (OIM) of the Piper Alpha said that he toured his platform every evening. He conceded he saw little as everyone had stopped work by then but explained it was the only time that was convenient.

It is of course vital that managers tour the site when it's busy if that's at all feasible. In a later chapter we explain the psychology behind why people cut corners but even without a detailed knowledge of ABC analysis it's easy to predict that more risks will be taken when the site is busy than when it's quiet. That said if logistics and safety issues mean that a 'busy' visit isn't possible very often then all is not entirely lost. If you ask the right questions in the right way, you'll still be able to appreciate what happens when it's busy. Later chapters show you how to do this.

It is of course vital that a meaningful number of observations and discussions be undertaken, and many organisations fail to achieve this critical amount so that when asked many workers will say that they haven't been subject to such an observation and discussion for months or even years. For a typical site for each employee to be talked to around once a quarter means each manager undertaking an ASM discussion around once a week.

This is a significant undertaking and the role of management commitment in ensuring it happens is paramount here

The Sailor's Challenge and Management Commitment

I gave a talk once with the sailor Peter Goss – made famous because he turned back in the Antarctic to rescue a French sailor that was out of range of the Australian rescue services. He saved the man with minutes to spare after first sewing his right arm back on with a knitting needle (that's an exaggeration but not by much – it's an incredible story).

Pete was asked how long did it take to decide to turn back and his answer (which he's waiting to give) is "about 10 seconds ... you do say 'that's all I need' but then you get on with it .... because it's the values of the sea. You don't need to think about it you just get on with it as it's what you do ...". His challenge is "these vision statements and then like do you own them as I own the values of the sea?" All you can hear are people shifting uncomfortably in their seats.

My experience is that productivity is always 10 out of 10 but safety less so. And a ten beats a nine when push comes to shove. A competitor likes to quote the Spice Girl's first hit here ... which is that you get the level of safety performance that you "really, really want, No more, no less". You can't just ask for it – you have to embed it and insist on it. I'd like to give a checklist of things that your supervisors and managers might be guilty of if you just ask for it.

- Doing something unsafe themselves because they are very experienced but saying "but you must never do this yourself"

- Saying "OK, just this once but be careful!"

- Asking about a safety input "how long is this going to take?" when they should have asked "how long do you need?"

- Starting a meeting with "as you know we need to get the safety stuff done first ..." (and clearly meaning "out of the way so we can get on with the important stuff")

- Communicating that by sitting back relaxed and calm whilst discussing safety but then leaning forward and becoming animated and focused when the topic of productivity comes up

- Leaking real meaning in a number of other ways that are less obvious such as getting the words in the wrong order! (At a subconscious level the word but in the middle of a sentence means ignore the first bit, the important thing is coming up so "do it safely but do it by Friday" means something very different to "do it by Friday but do it safely". (See a more detailed discussion in chapter 13).

And on top of all that people just know what's important to you by simply talking to you. You can ask me just about anything about the recent British Lions rugby tour of South Africa and I'll have lots of facts and opinions to throw into the conversation. On the other hand I don't know very much about the coming and goings at the local football club (Manchester City) though ... I mean I know they now have lots of Abu Dhabi money and a Welsh manager but that's about it. Just the headline stuff really ... you see I'm just not really that interested.

Summary of Main Points

- All workforces have a huge amount to contribute because they are the experts.

- You get the safety culture that you demonstrate you want with your actions, not the one you say you want.

- You need to demonstrate your commitment by walking the floor and focusing on, and discussing, safety.

CHAPTER 2

SAFETY CULTURE AND BEHAVIOUR

The first section made the point that to be effective, management really need to get out and devote some time to looking at and discussing safety exclusively. This section considers what to look for.

Models of Safety Culture

Parker and Hudson have a basic five factor model of safety culture that I find really useful. It is:

- Generative – a healthy paranoia about safety

- Proactive – see below

- Calculative (Compliant) – safety is managed on the basis of procedures and documentation and uses trail indicators

- Reactive – safety is an issue once something has occurred

- Pathological – safety is an inconvenience. Don't get caught!

Many organisations looking to improve their safety performance by addressing their human factors issues will find that they are squarely at the "calculative" stage of safety culture. That is, they have moved beyond 'reactive' and have good systems, procedures, training and inductions in place and have a set of files guaranteed to deliver a certificate or two for the wall in reception. Despite this baseline of achievement they know that the descriptions in the neat files and the reality in the middle of a busy shift can differ. Further, that this reflects a broader truth, which is that their safety performance has hit a plateau and has been like that for some time. Headline scores are typically waving around slightly as if in a narrow horizontal corridor of best and worst performance – known widely in the safety world as the infamous 'safety wave'. Experience is that the companies in question can easily identify that they need to 'do something' about the fact that 90% or more of incidents seem to have a key human element. It's deciding what to do to push through this plateau that is harder.

Perhaps a really good everyday example of the safety wave is dieting. There have been several well received books recently with titles along the lines of "which bit of 'dieting doesn't work' don't you understand?!" which point out that once the diet is over the old weight (plus a new pound or two) goes back on. To maintain weight loss they stress you simply need to make small but meaningful adjustment to your diet and exercise regimes and then stick with these new behaviours for ever!

Back with safety there are six clusters of behaviours that we think distinguish calculative from proactive companies:

- Communication - Now of course almost all companies communicate about safety but it's how well and how often that makes the difference. Casanova's reputation wasn't based on him having sex, badly, once a month!

- Workforce Involvement - Proactive companies have high levels of workforce involvement

- Modelling – In proactive companies managers always model safety themselves by (for example) following safety rules

- Challenging – In proactive companies managers challenge unsafe behaviour frequently and not just 'big' things but everyday unsafe acts too

- Analysis – Proactive companies analyse before they act and have a 'Just Culture' as described by James Reason and others

- Lead indicators – proactive companies actually use them!

Chapter 6 on the context of Affective Safety Management covers these issues in detail.

The 'Bradley Curve'

I'm aware that some companies may be more familiar with the 'dependency' model of safety culture or the 'Bradley Curve'. Broadly speaking, the first stage of this model is 'dependent', where people act safely so that they don't get into trouble. The second is 'independent', where people are safe so they don't get hurt, and the third and highest stage is 'interdependent', where people act safely so that no-one gets hurt. Parker and Hudson's 'proactive' and 'generative' categories are broadly analogous to 'interdependent'.

Latitude videos have a short film about Meerkats' interdependent 'safety culture' that gets these points across in a user-friendly way. The film describes the hostile environment in which they live and makes the point that if they didn't cooperate they wouldn't survive. A sleepy Meerkat trying to stay awake on sentry duty – and failing – is about as cute and memorable an image as a camera can capture. Though this film might seem quite light and fluffy on first viewing, in the appendix chapter on training we stress that making training memorable is vital.

Another very popular model of safety culture starts at a 'just compliant' level and moves up in five steps to somewhere near the border between 'proactive' and 'generative'. (These being "Emerging"; "Managing"; "Involving"; "Cooperating" and "Continually Improving"). I have found this tool cluttered and too descriptive: maybe others have too as I've seen this summarised as 'compliant' (I.E.. step one and half of step two) 'improving' and 'learning' – which again broadly fits Parker and Hudson's model. Again, 9 times out of 10, clients may be described as 'compliant but suffering from the plateau effect and wanting to push on from there'. I just find the Parker and Hudson model better fits that description.

Bradley and Parker and Hudson. A client recently asked us to undertake a safety culture survey but, as well as giving them formal feedback, they also wanted us to map it onto the Bradley Curve. (Because that is the terminology the managers in the field were most familiar with). When we looked into the Bradley concept in depth, however, we found that there didn't seem to be much behind it at all in the way of research. As far as we could tell it was a concept made up on the back of a cigarette packet deep in the heart of DuPont somewhere some decades back. More interestingly from a research perspective, however, some of the Bradley concepts such as trust and team-work that resonate so much around the world - though certainly overlapping with the Parker and Hudson model at the pro-active level - aren't really as well captured by the academic model as the Bradley notion seems to. So we upgraded our research tool from an academic five factor model to a six factor one which includes some new assessment items and a formal "Bradley" score.

Initially, clients seem to really like it and enthused then wrote it all up into an article published in the June 2009 edition of the Health and Safety Practitioner describing what we'd done and why. We admitted we were flying blind a bit here and asked for comments and (especially) corrections. So far the only comments have been positive ones so perhaps we can boast we've recently been able to enhance the understanding of safety culture models and that the most useful one is based solidly on the academic five-factor Parker and Hudson one with a twist of Bradley thrown in. (Again, corrections and observations are most welcome!).

Why "Try Harder" Only Works in the Short Term

Some people ask if it's all about people shouldn't we just get them to try harder? Sadly there isn't a magic bullet and although inspirational talks by the likes of Ian Whittingham certainly help, it is usually only in the short term. This is because increased effort and attention can take you only so far. Changing underlying attitudes and values is very difficult as anyone who has ever debated politics, sport or religion in the pub knows. Whether right or wrong it is true that most people simply do not change their attitudes. A practical illustration of this would be that just as a new football manager is required to deliver six points more from the first five games in charge before performance drifts back to the previous standard, so it is with safety. You can get close to 100% for a while but this simply isn't sustainable. (In football terms this might be "110% Brian" or even "150%". Am I being too judgmental when I find this almost compulsory statistical nonsense hugely irritating?)

Regardless, Martin O'Neil at Aston Villa would be a good example. Villa enjoyed an excellent start to the 2006/07 season, then tailed off following the end of the honeymoon but, because of the sensible changes he made on arrival at the club, Villa rose to a stronger finish and are enjoying an even better second season.

This simply reflects a universal truth – you cannot improve performance in the medium to long term without changing something and this will nearly always involve good management. Even very high impact events such as Hillsborough and September the 11th have had limited long term impact on people's day-to-day attitudes. It's often said that expecting a different end result from the same input is a classic sign of insanity! Returning to Parker and Hudson, the good news is that i) the behaviours that characterise proactive companies are all easy to do, in theory, at least and ii) are also the characteristic of companies that enjoy high levels of product quality, industrial relations, low stress and profitability. Therefore, though considerable effort is required to get to the end result, the "win-win" sell to senior line management is far from impossible.

This is important because as we are moving from a culture of guarding and legislative compliance to one of best practice and continuous improvement, it has become apparent that even large investments in managing and designing safety often deliver diminishing returns because the vast majority of accidents are now "behavioural" (UK HSE and industry figures suggest between 70 to 95%). So if companies are to progress their safety cultures they have to address the Human Factors/ Behavioural issues. A huge number of companies appreciate the need to do this and many have adopted an approach that focuses directly on "behaviour". There are any number of variations in the theme – some rather better than others – but collectively they are considered "behavioural safety". Many industries will have considerable direct experience of behavioural safety – for example pretty much all oil platforms in the North Sea will have run a process and many have run several. Other industries are coming to the field only now and construction is a good example.

Regardless, all companies that aspire to a strong safety culture need to address behaviour directly on a daily basis. This brings us to Heinrich's Triangle.

A Key Theory – Heinrich's Triangle

Heinrich's Triangle is the key theory behind the focus on the key behaviours that lead to accidents. The Triangle suggests that for every 330 unsafe acts at the bottom of the triangle, 30 of those unsafe acts will result in minor injuries and 1 in a major or lost time incident. The figures themselves don't stand up to much scrutiny. It's more like 1:300:3000, and there's the Bird Triangle and the Safety Iceberg too. However, the principle behind all of these always stands up in research. That is:

The bigger the bottom of the triangle the bigger the top

For example, say you cross the road each day without much care; say you're always listening to your iPod in a world of your own. The odds indicate that generally you'll "get away with it"; but over 330 crossings (over a year if you cross once a day) you'll have 30 near hits and might expect one major incident. Actually, in this particular instance the ratios are probably about right but then crossing the road is just about the most dangerous thing that most people do.

Here's an industrial example. Consider what is most likely to cause an injury on an oil or gas rig. Actually it's not holding the handrail when using stairs! Now say the chance of falling down and breaking your neck is one in 100,000. That's not much chance on a given day but if the stairs are used a million times a year and nobody holds the handrail then we are looking at around 10 accidents over a year. If 90% of people hold the hand rail, you'll have one accident give or take and if 99% of people hold it then there's about one accident every 10 years.

This isn't an academic example as about 50% of all lost time incidents offshore are caused by ... people falling down the stairs. This really isn't very convenient if the injured person is a specialist technician and the cost of having to heli-vac someone off the platform without a technically competent replacement can run into millions if product flow is disrupted. It's not surprising then that in this most dangerous of industries the behavioural approach has been eagerly embraced. One platform won an award for playing "Stairway to Heaven" over the tannoy as part of a 'hold the handrail' campaign. (They'd play 'Dedicated Follower of Fashion' on PPE awareness day... but I'm digressing.)

Heinrich and Gravity

No matter how sophisticated our safety culture, there is one risk factor we simply cannot design out completely; and that's gravity. Not if we want to move our product or people. If you look in any accident book you'll see that it is full of people who have had a gravity-related incident. Ian Whittingham's accident that was briefly mentioned in the introduction was that he fell 20ft through a fragile roof and landed on machinery. Likewise the 'handrail' figures from the offshore industry, while incidents involving celebrities nearly always involve gravity too – from the tragic (Eric Clapton's son falling from a window in New York) to the comic (Keith Richards falling out of a coconut tree). (The Keith Richards incident always reminds me of an old Welsh joke in which a father counsels his son "now, son don't you be drinking and driving, take some drugs and fly home instead!")

More seriously it's worth noting that the A&E department of any hospital will be full of people who've had a bad interaction with gravity. This is important as the lost time incident book of any company will be full of them and it's inevitable that any gravity-related incident will be at least in part behavioural. You simply cannot get to a zero incident culture without directly and effectively addressing day-to-day behavioural issues.

Heinrich and the Chain Effect ...

In practical terms most organisations will of course struggle to be entirely unsafe behaviour free – and this means that inevitably the bottom of the triangle will fill up and an accident will, at some point, happen. The better news is that most accidents involve a combination of behaviours and this gives us an opportunity to be proactive.

For example, several people a year will be killed by something coming off a scaffold. The five behaviours that combine here are:

- Poor housekeeping
- Someone unable to see where they are putting their feet – or maybe rushing
- Missing toe board
- Lack of isolation

And finally

- Missing hard hat

The important thing is that most of these behaviours need to occur for the fatality to happen. Break the chain at any point and the accident is avoided. For example, being hit on the head by something that would have killed you whilst you're wearing a hard hat is something of a shock... but you survive it. (Indeed the author survived it in 1993). What often happens, however, is that the scaffold clip or brick is kicked by the person who can't see where they are putting their feet and it is stopped by the toe-board. The person pauses; sees that the object would have landed near the people below without hard hats on – you say – and says "hmmm, that could have been nasty!" then walks on their way.

What no-one appreciates at the time is that without that toe-board someone would have been killed instantly.

Thousands of incidents like this happen all around the world on a daily basis – just one link in the chain holds and nothing happens and because it's not the fabled 'last line of defence' we never even know how close we were to disaster.

The excellent series of videos about the leading safety campaigner Ken Woodward contain an example of this. ("Ken's Story"; "The Witness" etc) Ken was blinded in a chemical explosion and though someone dragging him into a power shower nearby saved his life it couldn't save his eyes. Some years later it transpired that an engineer had come in on his day off to fix that shower – but was too modest to mention it until years later.

More Subtle Behaviours

As well as obvious behaviours like housekeeping, manual handling, looking in the direction of travel, beeping a horn at blind corners and PPE, there are more subtle daily events that are also vital. Consider a toolbox talk that is given half-heartedly by someone who mumbles. When the question is asked at the end "all ok with that?" no-one dissents and everyone signs to say they attended. But the impact of the talk will be minimal, possibly non-existent, on the two chaps at the back who can't speak English very well and so did not understand a word.

Heinrich and the "Tipping Point"

Have you ever been on a site where a group of electricians for example are breaking all the safety rules and seen them later at a different site where they are following them all – but without any apparent increase in supervision? I'd like to address the psychology behind that before considering the practical implications of this. Before we do that though - and to borrow a line from Monty Python - something completely different.

Imagine, if you would, that you went to a swingers club for the very first time. What would you do? (Please go with this – I'm trying to make an interesting analogy that illustrates a hugely important psychological construct in a memorable way – rather than just be smutty!). Obviously, you personally would be morally outraged and leave instantly … but imagine instead you're the sort of person who pops up on the TV shows shown around 10 o'clock on Channel 4 or 5 or Sky One on a weekend. You've never seen one episode of Eurotrash? On your first ever visit can I suggest you'd get yourself a drink and find a corner from which to observe what was going on and what you might see is, at a certain time, people drifting off and getting changed from civilian clothes to towels or skimpy underwear. If there were, say, 50 people there, would you be in the first 10 to go and get changed on your first visit? (Almost certainly not I'd argue). Would you be one of the last handful? (Well possibly in this situation but you'd probably feel very uncomfortable and 'out of place'). Research would suggest that you'd probably get changed once it was obvious you were in a clear minority.

What this demonstrates is 'modelling', which is where we tend to look about and see what everyone else does (especially the experienced confident ones) and feel under a lot of social pressure to copy them and fit in. Obviously, when considering safety we are talking about new starts and contractors here. They will look about and see "what's what" on arrival. I used to cite Buckingham Palace garden parties in an attempt to illustrate this point in a little less 'channel four late at night' style. However, when you point out that people won't, as they promised their friends, insist on a 'snake bite' or a pint of Brains SA but will instead accept the Pimms they've been offered some will tend to insist 'no I wouldn't!' And, without pre-recorded secret footage of them at a garden party it's difficult to resolve that one. In an attempt at a demonstration of this type of effect I once sent an entire audience out of a ballroom complete with coats and bags and folders then asked them to come back in and pointed out they were all sitting in exactly the same seats – with not 'taking' someone else's seat even if it's a better one being an entirely social convention of course. Naturally a hand went up and a chap said "ah! Now you see the reason I'm sitting here is…"

I was involved in the Cullen Inquiry into the Ladbroke Grove rail crash and though the final report was substantial one of the things we all agreed on was a definition of safety culture as "the typical behaviour".

Now if what these new starts and sub-contractors see when they look about is that half the people are safe and half are unsafe then they can follow either and not stand out. From a social norm perspective they have free choice. Now if 95% are acting safely that's a very different situation and there will be a "tipping point" – probably around 85% – where a new individual will feel under pressure to comply and act safely. This is especially important as recent research by Cialdini and others suggests that the power of social norms is even stronger than we first thought.

So, although there are a number of "behavioural approaches" on the market, in essence, the aim of them all should be to ensure we hit this "tipping point" at the very least where acting safely becomes self-sustaining at a peer level.

Summary of Main Points

- You won't improve things by trying to get people to try harder in the medium to long term – you have to change things
- The smaller the bottom of Heinrich's Triangle, the smaller the top of the triangle as fewer unsafe behaviours means fewer accidents
- Stopping just one unsafe behaviour in a behavioural chain will stop the accident
- If you get past the critical level (or Tipping Point) then safe behaviour becomes the norm – and norms are more important than we think

CHAPTER 3

SAFETY CULTURE AND PSYCHOLOGY

Some of the founders of the 'Affective Safety' concept drew heavily on these fields of work. Although the author hasn't anywhere near the depth of knowledge of these individuals to comment with any authority – and won't refer to them directly again in this book – I do think it's important to try and make a broad overview for contextual reasons. Further I'd very much hope that an expert would agree that nothing in the book contradicts the basic principles espoused in these fields. Well, the non-controversial ones anyway! (If you are an expert and think it does please let me know).

Emotional Intelligence

We have a team-building exercise based on the Belbin team roles questionnaire that seeks to show individuals that we all have strengths and weaknesses and that for a team or organisation to flourish they have to seek to maximise their strengths and minimise the impact of their weaknesses. Discussion of the strengths and weaknesses of a natural "Monitor Evaluator" pretty well explains what emotional intelligence is.

People who are natural 'Monitor Evaluators' tend to be clever and naturally adept at stepping back and taking a helicopter overview of what's going wrong. When they interject it's nearly always to say something astute, but how they say it becomes key. Have you ever worked with anyone whose natural style is to say "we've gone off on a tangent again …I said we would if we didn't do X … it's all gone wrong … we'll never get finished at this rate … Oh, … I … give … up!? You lot are useless!"

Did you perhaps find that that wasn't very helpful and productive?!

I once ran a development centre for senior managers at a large industrial company. During the de-brief session I had to deal with an individual whose scores for team work were awful but whose intelligence was incredible – off the scale on a full battery of high level tests. Putting him straight was easy, I just needed to point out that not only was he nearly always going to be the most intelligent person in the room, he was probably the most intelligent man in the company and all he needed to do to enhance his input was to have a lot more patience with his colleagues and develop a coaching style. The feedback from his director a year later was encouraging "He's been flying since he calmed down and stopped winding everyone up by constantly sighing and rolling his eyes in meetings!"

How to apply any natural intelligence we may have effectively (and should that also be affectively) is what this book is primarily about.

Neuro Linguistic Programming (NLP)

This is a fascinating field not without controversy but full of cracking tips and observations. For example, it's suggested that what we find most annoying in other people are in fact our own faults! So if we find ourselves getting irate about a minor fault in others … we might be advised to get a mirror out! (When I stop mid moan about something and ask my partner "I do this myself don't I?" the answer is nearly always "oh yes …".)

Most important for our purposes though, is the basic principle that we have control of how we respond to the world around us. We don't have to be passive. So for example, if we sit for ten minutes wishing the world wasn't the way it is or wishing that things that have happened hadn't happened … then we have achieved nothing and wasted ten minutes. A famous example would be that in every conversation he had with a prison guard Nelson Mandela tried to ensure his incarceration on Robben Island was productive.

The Useless Corporal – A True Story. At the end of a war a useless corporal was hospitalised with shell shock. Normally these prisoners would be shouted at and bullied into going back to the front but the Doctor treating him tried a different tack because he felt this chap really wasn't malingering and wanted to get better. He told him that God had chosen him as a leader of his people, that he had untapped potential and that his country needed him and so on. This was all nonsense really as he had proved a useless soldier up to this point and was only made corporal because most of his comrades were dead and he could contribute little as the war finished soon after anyway. However, some time later he walked into a meeting of a new political party and buoyed by new-found self-belief contributed greatly with questions and suggestions from the back of the hall. Soon he was on the stage at the front, soon after that he became regional leader and he didn't stop until, in his over confidence, he attacked Russia and suffered the same fate as Napoleon. He was of course Adolf Hitler.

When seeking a role model who demonstrates what can be achieved with a positive approach we are perhaps better sticking with Nelson Mandela of course. Though, is it just me, or is it more frequent to meet managers who seem to have modelled themselves on Napoleon?

Expectations and Self-fulfilling Prophecies

Imagine a man who comes into his local pub. He's quite 'popular' though you're not sure why – you don't warm to him yourself – but popular he is. He's recently had a win on the lottery and offers to buy everyone a drink. Is he being 'flash' or 'generous'? Maybe he doesn't offer anyone a drink but just quietly takes his normal seat. Is he being mean or modest? Imagine a second chap. He isn't very popular – you're not sure why as he seems fine to you – but he isn't. He has had a win on the lottery and offers to buy everyone a drink. Is he being generous or flash? Or maybe he doesn't offer anyone a drink but just quietly takes his normal seat. Is he being modest or mean? Sometimes you just can't win because we often see what we expect to see. And, of course it is true for most practical purposes that perception is reality.

Worse than this we will actively seek out evidence that supports our position rather than evidence that contradicts this. Consider that you are shown four cards and told they are double-sided with a letter on one and a number on the other. They are laid out for you like so:

A   B   7   8

And you are told that the rule is that if there is an A on the front there will be a 7 on the back. How many do you need to turn over to decide if that rule is true? (Please have a go at that quickly before reading on).

Instinctively, studies show that most people will turn over the A and then think a bit and turn over the 7 too – but turning over the later card proves nothing as the rule is about what's on the back of an A card. You could find an A, and X or a picture of a pink elephant – none of them are relevant. So it's the 8 we need to turn over as finding an A there would disprove the rule. We make this mistake because we will instinctively seek evidence to confirm that something is true.

Expectations. Now, this is problematic for a Just Culture where a new start or a sub-contractor who, objectively speaking, should be given the benefit of the doubt but isn't. (Or the popular old hand who really shouldn't but is…). However, it gets worse because of the "self-fulfilling prophecy". This is where we actually do get the behaviour we expect – but primarily because we expected it. It's easy to imagine a racist getting surly service from someone of a different colour or caste because the racist is rude and off-hand – but it works in the world of work too. In a classic piece of research, a writer called McGregor talks of "theory X and theory Y". Some managers are naturally "theory X", he says – they expect workers to be lazy and in need of constant supervision and discipline. On the other hand some are naturally "theory Y" – expecting workers to be reliable, conscientious and motivated so light supervision and delegation are the order of the day. Studies show that whilst some workers will of course take full advantage of the trusting Y type – the vast majority don't and that pretty much everyone that is treated in a theory X way behaves in a theory X way.

"Hearts and Minds" and "Above the Line" Behaviour

"Above the line" behaviours (or what some call "organisational citizenship behaviours") are such as contributing suggestions, looking out for new starts in their green hats, volunteering to be involved in new initiatives and schemes, and attending social events. Lots of organisations express themselves very keen to encourage these behaviours in the workforce – or simply bemoan their absence, lamenting that "we just can't seem to win the hearts and minds of the workforce – important as it is and try as we might!"

A key premise of this book is that many of these things will flow very naturally in a proactive and 'Just' safety culture. Before moving on to the day-to-day practicalities of an Affective Safety culture it must be conceded that most of the things suggested in it are difficult to achieve because they require time and effort in the form of strong leadership from the top, training, formal follow-up – and informal follow-up on a daily basis. All change is difficult. On the other hand, I'd argue that all of what follows falls in the dinner party putdown that all safety psychologists have heard. Having been asked, "What exactly does safety psychology entail then?" It's invariable that anyone who listens to the answer will observe:

"But that's just common sense that is!"

Summary of Main Points

- There's being clever and there's being able to apply that cleverness effectively. They are not the same thing!

- You are what you do – not what you think you are deep down.

CHAPTER 4

HUMAN FACTORS AND SAFETY BEHAVIOUR

This chapter addresses, for contextual purposes, three current controversies in the field of human factors. These are organisational maturity, 'no name, no blame' and behaviourally focused safety i.e. blaming the worker. You will see that all three debates share a common theme, which is that when you step back and stress the importance of analysis there isn't actually any controversy at all. There are also brief notes on an old issue – does understanding and articulating any problems help the HSE?

Organisational Maturity

There is a popular argument that organisations should not attempt a behavioural approach until all traditional approaches have been utilised. Indeed maturity models have been produced by such as the Keil Centre to help measure "readiness" specific to the offshore industry. Essentially this model sensibly suggests that all offshore companies have mature systems but that the maturity of organisational behaviours differs between companies. Companies should therefore systematically work their way up the maturity model before attempting to apply the more "sophisticated" behavioural systems. Martin Anderson, in an excellent article in the March 2008 edition of the Safety and Health Practitioner, gives a long list of things that organisations should focus on:

- HAZOP or other assessment completed

- Hierarchy of control applied

- Accurate operating procedures are available for all eventualities including emergencies

- Operatives being fully trained - not just in the basics but so they can troubleshoot should things go wrong.

- The site has the required operating capacity re staffing levels and experience

- Lessons have been learned from site, company and industry

- Succession planning ensures knowledge is retained

- Safety management and risk control measures have been reviewed to ensure they remain usable and relevant.

Unfortunately, he seems to suggest that "behavioural interventions will only be successful and … should only be attempted" when companies have satisfied the above. At first glance this certainly seems a sensible enough approach but for the author it is too academic and analytical as it misses a key point and I'd therefore like to argue that this is not exactly a reckless and impetuous position to take!

First, people get confused about what the best behavioural approaches are. Now although the very best ones have high levels of workforce involvement and may even utilise the workforce in collecting measures, the key element of a behavioural approach, however, is to set people up to undertake proactive behavioural analysis so that the organisation can understand why any unsafe behaviour is occurring. The answers may well plug directly into the above list – or be simpler and easy to action. (I don't wear these gloves because they don't fit; buy different sizes, for example). This sort of analysis is easy to achieve through safety leadership training and/ or the setting up of a time limited workforce project team. It really doesn't need a timeconsuming and bureaucratic process that detracts from the big picture.

The main point is that root-cause analysis actually aids any work on systems improvements by highlighting existing weaknesses from another angle. Management's resolve to respond effectively to this flood of information and data may well be tested – but many "immature" organisations from industry in general have done so very successfully. (And by this we mean immature in systems terms never mind "organisational behaviour"). They simply needed (even) higher levels of management commitment than "mature" organisations.

However, since experience suggests an organisation will struggle to achieve any sort of lasting change without a decent level of management commitment it's almost an entirely academic point!

For example, "trust" is often a key element of safety maturity models. Imagine a workforce team set up to undertake some behavioural analysis. They come up with a handful of high-impact low-cost solutions about such issues as PPE and traffic flow and are thanked for their contributions both in person and through a newsletter. It's not difficult to run the project as all companies can resource projects. It's what they do. However, is there any sort of top down system approach that could remotely approach an increase in trust in such a time scale?

Baker Report. I'd argue that one of the key findings of the Baker report on the 2005 Texas City explosion could prove problematic here if misunderstood. Clearly, it is possible that organisations may get sidetracked by numbers and statistics and over focus on the (behavioural) accidents they are having and not on the (process) accidents they are (not yet) having. The learning point "don't forget basic process!" is, of course, 100 per cent valid. However, this really isn't an either/or situation. Companies can and should do both. A friend who is a very senior HSE inspector told me a story of visiting an oil refinery and being told to 'hold the handrail' just after noting down three serious process issues that he felt needed urgent attention. He said that he was still feeling indignant when he "damn nearly fell down the stairs and broke my neck" a few minutes later. That says it all really.

Safety Climate and Safety Culture

It might be worth distinguishing between safety climate and safety culture. Climate is essentially a short-term perspective and can be influenced by such things as motivational speakers or significant events. There was for example a quite strong anti-royalist climate around the time of Princess Diana's death but the UK doesn't really seem to have a strong Republican culture and 'the Firm' seem to have broadly recovered from these events. However, there does, over the decades, seem to be a cultural drifting of support away from the monarchy and this perhaps illustrates the timescales that can be involved here without the committed application of an effective strategy. Similarly, following a serious incident at a site a safety aware climate may pervade for a few months but if no fundamental changes are made in the way the work is organised then the underlying culture will re-establish itself soon enough. The distinction is important as when assessing an organisation's safety culture we often stress that in-depth and anonymous group discussions are better as it's easier to tease out deep-rooted issues with anecdotes and examples.

Behavioural Focused Safety is "Blaming the Victim"

Some recent papers in the safety literature have criticised "behavioural safety" for focusing "on the victim and not the hazards". This is partially a political agenda – as the writers are nearly all pro-union who believe safety should be part of their brief (and who, to be fair, do appear to have good evidence to support their view that effective safety representatives more often than not mean a strong safety culture). Regardless, any good behaviourist can remain aloof from this wider debate – their brief being to focus on what "is", not on what should be or even what they'd prefer. (Several requests for a right to reply in the main magazine that pushes this view or a public debate with the authors have been made and, tellingly perhaps, all have been declined).

However, it must be accepted that many "awareness" or "personal values" - based approaches with a "behavioural safety" tag are guilty as charged! There is an ever increasing number of programmes with a "behavioural safety" tag on the market whose only link with behavioural safety is adding the expression to their glossy brochure – then running exactly the same "personal values/ team building/empowerment" course as always – except throwing in the word "safety" now and then.

As above, because some "80% to 95% of all accidents are caused by people" it is easy to assume the only meaningful way to improve safety is to make people "be safer", but focusing too closely on the person is far too limiting. As we keep saying behavioural change is primarily brought about not by changing the person but by changing their environment.

Behavioural safety can help add to the pressure for change by the strength of its analysis and the quality of its pro-active data.

The author saw an interesting twist on this at a recent conference. A union chap presented saying that all this "85% of accidents are caused by people stuff is crap". In his view 90% of what goes on in a company is down to management … and he is of course both right and wrong. Basically if the company is starting from scratch it's down to management to design a safe process, provide guards and training, ensure management systems are in place and audit them frequently. However, many companies have already done all that pretty well. They are "calculative" in Parker and Hudson terms and broadly compliant … and from here on in it really is the people we need to focus on as much as the systems!

In his article Martin Anderson stresses that "Addressing behaviours must not be seen as an alternative to ensuring that adequate engineering design and effective safety management systems are in place … though large advances have been made in engineering and safety management systems, major accidents are still occurring due to failures in these aspects. It is not appropriate to conclude we have solved engineering causes of accidents". (SHP March 2008). He goes on to conclude very rightly in my view that "Management decisions should not be excluded from the behavioural safety process".

And so say all of us. But it really doesn't need to be an "either/ or". If the first question asked in a behavioural approach is 'why?' it's wholly congruent.

"No Name, No Blame" and 'Just Culture'

The author was on an oil platform undertaking a safety culture audit and was told:

"We have no name no blame on this platform but management really like to know who it is they're not blaming!"

"No Name No Blame" or NNNB is a much misunderstood expression. It should obviously not be applied to all safety situations per se as where would that leave personal responsibility to say nothing of the legal position? James Reason's concept of **Just Culture** stresses that all environmental issues are explored fully before any individual is blamed and/or disciplined. Much of his work was undertaken in the aviation industry and he gives an example that, for me, illustrates the principle perfectly.

Imagine a man checking rivets on a plane who has the gantry to get close, a torch and the time to do it. He does it conscientiously but misses one. This is human error and we should invent a machine that works more effectively than the human eye. Imagine now a man checking rivets who hasn't a torch and/or who hasn't a gantry and/or who hasn't the time. He does the best job he can under the circumstances but misses one. This is the company's fault and he is broadly blameless. Finally, imagine a man who has the time, the torch and a gantry but who does the job quickly from the ground so that he can get back to his crossword. This is his fault and he should suffer accordingly.

A more in-depth analysis would of course ask questions such as had the employee been trained properly in what to look for? Had a supervisor previously seen the person 'rush it' but said nothing? Then there are issues of individual responsibility to challenge and so on. For the purposes of making the basic model clear please assume that the answers to these questions are, respectively, yes and he did but was basically ignored.

Errors and Violations. The basic model says that unsafe behaviour can fall into two categories – errors and violations. Errors are unintended and can be caused by, for example, human fallibility, fatigue, badly designed equipment and/or maybe lack of training. These are issues that need to be addressed by Human Factors specialists and ergonomists and beyond the scope of this book. More interesting for us, perhaps are the violations because these are caused . These are categorized by the model as either:

- Individual
- Optimizing
- Situational

The individual violation is as described above. A worker bang to rights who is doing his or her own thing for his or her own reasons. An optimizing violation means one where the worker takes a risk because they think that's what the company wants. For example, imagine a worker who has done a job on time with no near misses but with some corners cut. The feedback they get is "Great job! Well done!". Nothing else. The company is teaching them to do that again. Indeed, if you want to be emotive about it you could call that *grooming*.

A situational violation is one where the individual is in a situation where cutting corners is considered unavoidable. This happens often with peripatetic workers of course and issues of contracts, resources and 'job and knock' will nearly always become apparent as soon as you scratch the surface here. A less controversial example would be with fork lift truck drivers in factories. We all know the training… "stop, apply handbrake and commence lifting forks…". Is there a fork lift driver in the world that follows these rules to the letter? If there is – what time do they get to go home?

Situational overlaps with optimizing I think, in many respects and making the distinction can be difficult. (I sometimes think in practise it's just easier to ask "is this an individual or a situational/ optimizing" violation?) For example it's inconceivable that the FLT driver in the factory will not have been seen not following the rules. (Incidentally, from a behavioural perspective what's important is distinguishing between the driver who approaches the load smoothly, raising the forks only when with a pallet length or two of the load - so only a suicidal pedestrian could get hurt – and one who charges around the yard forks raised).

An interesting question I like to ask at workshops involves picturing a new worker with a perfect attitude to safety. They have a photograph of their children in their pocket to remind them to take no risks at all. However, there are a few unsafe behaviours that are undertaken by most of the workforce... and when they see the new start go the long way around they say nothing ... but the smirks and sniggers are obvious. The questions is, assuming the new start is pretty normal – how long before they start to cut the corner too? A week? Less?

The interesting question is how would you catagorise this behaviour? - as an individual violation or as a situational/ optimizing one? I haven't yet had a workshop that didn't plump en bloc for situational/optimizing – but we always agree that how that might play in a court of law, if it came to that, would be interesting. A key theme of the book is that it shouldn't come to that. This is an in built systemic problem on a par with an unguarded machine and should be looked for, and dealt with, just as systematically.

The key point is that whether it's an error or a situational/optimizing violation it's an organizational issue not primarily down to the individual. Indeed experience suggests that only about one time in ten is it the person who's primarily responsible. So addressing this problem with a "try harder, how many times do we have to remind you of the rules" tool box talk simply isn't ever going to get a company very far because it's not addressing the root cause of the problem in 90% of the cases. (Worse than that the one in ten who should be listening aren't – for reasons we'll explain later).

"No Name" and Workforce Processes. However, we'd argue that "NNNB" should always apply to a workforce behavioural safety programme. Although they may often be tempted to try to find out, management must not be allowed to "know who it is they're not blaming". This because:

- It helps with any measurement (and feedback) if there are any lead indicators being used as employees will act more naturally;

- It helps with root-cause analysis as employees will respond more frankly and honestly;

- It helps with ownership and involvement as volunteers from the shop floor are more likely to volunteer if there can never be any comeback because a "crap list has generated some crap". Further, workers are less likely to incur the ire of their colleagues if their safety discussions are entirely geared to root-cause analysis and not towards any sort of confrontation.

Our experience is that as soon as one manager comes over all John Wayne and demands names so he can "sort it out" anything with a volunteer element has a life expectancy of about five minutes. So for us it's Just Culture unless it's a workforce-owned process in which case it's no name, no blame – with the process focusing simply on analysis and (anonymous) data collection.

Management Errors

A key principle of this book is that it's rarely the worker being foolish or reckless that primarily causes an accident – it's nearly always the environment they find themselves in that's more important. This implicates management in the way they run the company and set up the tasks of course and I'd like to describe some classic errors of decision making that we *all* make – and frequently too.

Imagine you go on holiday with children to somewhere hot and exotic where the children will spend half their time in the sea. After drowning would you be most concerned about sharks or coconuts? Unless you've heard this before you'll probably say the sharks of course – but in truth deaths because of falling *coconuts* are about 10 times as common as death by shark attack (around 200 and 20 fatalities pa worldwide respectively).

This erroneous perception of risk is probably driven in part by perhaps our most instinctive, primeval and ancient fear … that of being eaten alive by another animal. That's fair enough perhaps! On the other hand it's also a good example of the "**availability heuristic**" (a heuristic is an intuitive judgement) and understanding this and other common mistakes of risk perception can help us understand why we make so many mistakes in safety management decision making.

Problem One – Availability Heuristic. The availability heuristic basically says that we'll give more weight to evidence that is most readily available to us to recall. For example, we'll be very aware of the risk of cancer if one or more loved ones has recently been a victim and it's at the forefront of our minds. Similarly we'll be very aware of a risk factor that's been all over the media like SARS or Bird flu – or shark attacks! Indeed experts like Prof Brian Toft FIIRSM say that risk perception is somewhere between extremely subjective and *entirely* subjective! And of course perception is reality.

Problem Two – Emotional Reasoning. Another major problem can be what you might call the "**invincibility cloak**". You might call this Freudian denial, optimistic overconfidence or just plain *foolishness* – but some people or organisations seem to genuinely believe that nothing bad will ever happen to them. This is because they have a deep-rooted confidence that "it'll be OK" and perhaps "just love the smell of napalm in the morning". Technically this is known as "emotional reasoning" a belief that what you *feel* must be true. This is of course the flip side of psychologists' work persuading people that they *can* safely travel by plane because they hardly ever crash and it's actually much safer than driving.

Problem Three - Selective Learning (Bias to the *Positive*). We recently had a client ask if they could visit a 'live' site as part of the project commissioning process. I warned them that I would of course pick a friendly and successful site and recommended that they challenge me to send them to an organisation that was struggling with the methodology. They thanked me for my advice, totally ignored it, had a lovely positive day out and came back and commissioned some work. In doing so they demonstrated another systemic problem we can face …which is that we much *prefer* to learn from the *positive* than from the *negative* even though we *all* know the truth of the maxim that ends " … and the wisest one learns from the **mistakes** of *others*". The word 'prefer' is highlighted as again preference is of course entirely subjective.

So we find in practise that, in an attempt to filter out all information that doesn't match our pre-existing mindset, we can actually walk past several negative learning opportunities until we find just one positive one that we declare is "most like us". Here this combines with another classic mistake of reasoning - "over generalisation" - which means to come to a general conclusion on limited data.

Problem Four – Hindsight and the Fundamental Attribution Bias (FAE). Perhaps the most problematic mindset we see is the one that has us believe it's always the person not following the rules that's causing all the problems - not perhaps the rules themselves. Studies show that whilst we all have our own particular biases we *all* consistently overestimate the importance of the *person* and underestimate the importance of the *environment* when assessing a situation. Worse, studies show that the worse the **outcome** the greater the bias. So when things go wrong we over blame the person and can give too little emphasis to the time pressures, or the (lack of) tools and equipment, or the training (or its absence), or the way supervisors routinely praise efficient but slightly risky work….

This can of course turn into a rather long list.

An interesting and important variation on the "FAE" is **hindsight bias**. We all know how incredibly easy it is to be wise after the event and many people will find themselves insisting they *knew* things were about to go badly wrong but no-one listened to their warnings. Or perhaps they didn't give any warnings because they felt that they would just be ignored.

A problem here is that this hindsight bias becomes *reality* in peoples' heads and we can find ourselves judging the individuals involved too harshly. Naturally where we all agree that it was all Xs fault and that frankly, we wouldn't have done that in their shoes it can really hinder learning if the truth is that actually we *would*.

Problem Five - Cognitive Dissonance. Forgive the psychobabble expression but "cognitive dissonance" is basically the formal term for where our actual behaviours and our stated attitudes diverge. The problem is that we can find it is far easier to "fudge" than to deal with this dissonance objectively. An example that we all face is drinking and driving **under** the limit. We know that driving whilst impaired by drink is dangerous and most of us know that driving legally but close to the limit is twice as dangerous as wholly sober driving. So when we come out of the pub or restaurant and it's late and raining we have the following choices.

We can say "Driving is dangerous enough at the best of times and especially risky at this time of night so I'll leave the car and queue for a bus in the rain or wait for an expensive taxi and deal with the inconvenience of fetching the car in the morning". Yes *quite* ... which leaves us with the following two possible internal conversations:

Option one: "sometimes I have to admit I push my luck ... I guess I'm not as safe as I'd like to think I am! I need to plan these nights out better or someone's going to get hurt" or do we go for option two: "I'll drive ... but I'll slow down, give myself even more room than usual and concentrate twice as hard. And besides what with me already being rather better than the average driver anyway ...". And Freud's concepts of *rationalisation* and *denial* hove into view ...

> This can be problematic at work at an individual level where we may see new workers saying "this behaviour doesn't seem safe to me – it makes me uncomfortable. My values are that I think of my family first and don't put myself at risk". They could then go the long way around every day and ignore the smirks and teasing of their colleagues but as we pointed out earlier we know that they don't. It's much easier for the individual to get back into equilibrium by "deciding" that "This lot have been around since year dot and they seem ok ... so I guess it's not that unsafe after all". Actually, of course, it still is. This can apply at an organisational or industry wide level too.

Problem Six - Groupthink. As you can imagine groupthink is where a group of like minded individuals get together and pretty much blindly agree on some matter – with little regard to alternative views and hard facts. Every reader will have a hatful of examples where this has proved costly in some way. (The "Bay of Pigs" failed invasion of Cuba fiasco was the first example officially labelled a "groupthink problem").

Studies suggest that the more cohesive the group generally the more likely it is and the more pressure any dissenting voice is likely to come under. Linking to this one of the most influential papers in the world of social sciences was published by Ben Schneider who argued we need to actively manage individual diversity as organisations will naturally *attract* a certain type of person, then tend to *select* those who best match the companies profile and then tend to have those who fit in least well most likely to *leave*. He called this ASA theory (attraction, selection, attrition). This automatically makes organisations natural environments for groupthink wouldn't you agree?

On an international level it has been suggested that groupthink played a significant part in the Challenger disaster. Despite the engineers at Morton Thiokol insisting that it was too cold to launch the Challenger and (initially) having the support of their management team the decision was changed when NASA 'leant' on them to toe the party line. The key moment was when the most senior person in the debate commented "I won't overrule the contractors decision - but frankly I'm appalled at their no fly position". After a furious in-house debate it was agreed that maybe they were being over cautious after all. Dissenting (engineering) voices were ignored as the others closed ranks with one manager actually telling the engineering manager to "take off his engineering hat and put on his management hat". As you well know they certainly weren't being over cautious at all …

What to do? As well as managing diversity and bringing in fresh eyes, organisations need to get into the habit of benchmarking with similar organisations. That said, much can be learned from organisations and industries that are *not* so similar.

Recently, I was at a recent industry association event where a perceived weakness that all delegates agreed on was the difficulty they had learning from each other – but who listened intently to a speaker from a different industry. Perhaps "not invented here" syndrome applies less strongly where it's "not invented *anywhere near here!*"

It's of course also useful to carry out "what if?" scenarios where delegates deliberately debate the very worst that might happen. Checking assumptions with both in-depth quantitative and qualitative assessments is also essential - so the likes of safety culture benchmarking are key here as of course are lead measures and good old fashioned problem solving in teams training. (By which we mean systematic coverage of the above as well as - or even *instead* of - "lets have a great laugh building a raft out of twigs and empty beer cans then get pissed back at the hotel" training).

Another simple brainstorming exercise is to write down the pros and cons of your point of view and then the pros and cons of that of an *opponent*. You'll find that the two boxes that are quickly full are **your** *pros* and **their** *cons*. You find that learning to fill *all* boxes *equally* is a really useful technique if only in preparation for a negotiation! Another interesting exercise is to force one member of a team of 5 or so to do nothing but strategic overview and monitor evaluation work in a problem solving exercise. Nine times out of ten you'll find they outperform a basic team of 5.

It is a scientific truth that outside of a lucky fluke the limits of effective safety management are set by the limits of objectivity - because how else can you most effectively and accurately identify risks and target resources? We'd like to argue that maximising objectivity is far harder than might be apparent at first glance. As ever the way forward is some well targeted training of an organisation's key individuals followed by the systematic application of the principles learned.

Individual Propensity to Accidents – Are there Accident Prone People?

The point is made repeatedly in the book that Human Error is unavoidable and that they key is not only minimising the likelihood of an error, but maximising the chance the person who makes the mistake will notice it and be able to recover. I hope that from a "just" culture perspective it's been made clear that the last person we should look at is the individual as so much of what goes wrong is systemic. That said, having given decision making fallibility a good going over it's worth addressing the question "are some people more prone to error than others?" And since there is an obvious and short answer to that question - if this is something of any use to organisations?

Would you want your family to be in the hands of a pilot who was easily bored and distracted, low in conscientiousness, prone to day dreaming, hugely risk tolerant, unintelligent, easily tired, and prone to mood swings? Personally I'd like them in the hands of someone conscientious, focused, risk aware, emotionally stable, physically robust and clever thank you very much and if it's all the same to you. (You also wouldn't want the pilot to have been Korean circa 1995. I'll get back to this in detail in a few pages).

A chap once said to me in a smoke shack "Tim, this Just Culture stuff is all well and good but there's a couple of muppets out there I wouldn't trust to walk my dog!" I'd like to leave the minority of muppets to one side if I can and concentrate on the *typical* worker and how individual variations within a normal band can impact on safety. This section, therefore, covers personality, intelligence (and its different types) and motivational drivers. I'd try to illustrate the points with reference to a true case study relating to a lack of containment at a chemical company. (At a glance caused by an incompetent management who'd made a lot of mistakes in the weeks leading up to the incident).

Individual Differences - Background Theory

Firstly, some background theory. Experts (EG Boyle, 2009) say that individual differences can be categorised into three broad types:

- Physical – size etc
- Physiological – for example health and fitness.
- Psychological – essentially intelligence, personality and motivation.

Physical and Physiological. It's obvious that large clumsy and badly co-ordinated individuals undertaking complicated tasks are more likely to have bumps. It's also obvious that unfit or poorly individuals will be more prone to tiredness - and that tired people make more mistakes and have more slips. We also know that badly designed shift systems or jobs with excessive physical or psychological strain can make people unnaturally tired and therefore accident prone.

What this section asks is if the *individual* differences that we can do little about because they are *innate* to the individual in question. I'd therefore like to describe how different types of **personality, motivation** and **intelligence** can interact to cause stress, poor performance and safety issues. As you can imagine things can get really complex here as intelligence, motivation and personality aren't simple things but are multi-faceted, complex and interact in any number of ways.

Intelligence. The basic types of **intelligence** are:

- verbal;
- numerical and
- spatial

In addition 101 others have been identified and described such as "musical" and "emotional". Emotional intelligence for example has had a lot of coverage in recent years but is far more about day to day habits of behaviour and interpersonal skills of course and overlaps with personality hugely. (Golman,1987). Mechanics and engineers can often be highest in *spatial* intelligence as can the likes of Wayne Rooney and David Beckham whose ability to instantly identify the weight and direction of a pass is so impressive.

As you can imagine intelligent people usually make fewer mistakes than unintelligent ones all else being equal. However, this isn't always the case and studies show how intelligent people can be more likely to switch off when faced with mundane tasks. It's said that peak performance is achieved between around 40 to 70% emotional arousal. If we are working at less than that and we are bored and prone to distraction, more than 70% and we are stressed. Hence the old adage "brain surgeons make for crap taxi drivers".

So matching the person to the task is always an important factor.

Personality. There are any number of models based on everything from Freud's Id and Ego through colour based models – originally based on the writing of Hippocrates with green being phlegmatic and so on - and even Simpson's characters! (Don't laugh "Simpson" profiles can be surprisingly astute as well as interesting – you really don't want to be Homer!). For what it's worth collated research, however, has focused on the "Big Five" factors of Extroversion; Anxiety; Conscientiousness; Open-Mindedness and Agreeableness.

My PhD used these factors to predict suicidal behaviour in army recruits. You won't be surprised to hear that we found that the army took anyone half sensible who would give basic training a go and then let that basic training sort out the ones who wanted to stay. The problem was that it wasn't just that the ones low in conscientiousness made mistakes – but that anxious ones were really worried about it. (On top of this the introverts hated barrack life so anyone low in conscientiousness as well as anxious and introverted tended to be having a *horrible* time).

In a substantial piece of research collating the findings of dozens of studies and based on the "big five" factors Clarke and Robertson (2005) found that personality factors such as conscientiousness and aggression did indeed correlate significantly with accident rates.

The actual figures are interesting and illustrate the point. Though careless, over confident sloppy people have more accidents than careful cautious people it's just a statistically significant correlation but not a perfect correlation by any means. The reason of course is (as was reiterated above) that usually it's the **environment** that is more important.

Motivation. I'd recommend Peter Warr's "Vitamin" model as perhaps the best description of what **motivates** people at work. His factors cover basic issues such as "money", "prestige" and "control" through more complex issues like "role clarity" (IE "I like to know what I need to do and hate vagueness" and "I like to understand how what I'm doing fits into the bigger picture"). You could call it the academic version of the phrase "different strokes for different folks".

A related but simpler model of motivation (Vroom's model) explains why so many safety initiatives fail. It says that our motivation to do something is a factor of multiplying:

1 We're clear what we need to do multiplied by

2 We expect that doing it will lead to success and

3 We value the outcome.

As the three are *multiplied* a nought anywhere gives an overall score of nought. It's a model well worth considering when we ask why a usually motivated supervisor hasn't embraced a new safety initiative. It's often because the training was vague and didn't make clear what was required, or perhaps because they just don't believe it will work.

The Real Incident. In order to illustrate how all these psychological factors can interact with a specific job and lead to error I'd like to introduce you to Steve who is the "incompetent manager" I mentioned above. Frankly if you'd seen Steve's performance in the weeks leading up to the accident it would have been easy to dismiss him as useless - an "accident waiting to happen".

Before describing what actually happened to Steve however here's a simplified list of some individual differences relating to task, personality and intelligence (as above) and my estimate of Steve's rating on these on a 1 to 5 scale.

Intelligence

Spatial intelligence (working out how objects interact)	*****
Numerical Intelligence	***
Verbal Intelligence	***
Musical Intelligence	*****

Natural Ability/ Personality/ Preference For

Being in charge	*
Working in a team	****
Task Clarity	*****
Job Security	*****
Power, Influence and Money	**
Strategic Planning	*

I'm sure you can see that Steve was ideally suited to solving engineering problems as part of team on a day-to-day basis. "Today's engineering problem is this…" and off he went. Then he went home, played with the kids and played his music. He was a fulfilled, *highly competent* and contended man. Then because he was the best in the team he was promoted and felt he couldn't say no. (As you can see from the profile he's a bit timid and doesn't like to say no because he hates confrontation. Further, his family can use the money as his *less* that timid wife made clear). Worse, after a swift round of "rightsizing" he was promoted again. He was now in charge of process safety for a large and dangerous plant and was of course liaising with HR re a whole raft of training courses identified as relevant.

The task was difficult and vague and all about budgets, strategy and man management … and despite having the right *technical* qualifications he was just not very good at it. Indeed his emotional arousal was a long way north of 70% and you wont be surprised to learn that he got very stressed, very quickly and started making mistakes. Lots of them. A month or so later the incident occurred.

Korean Culture and Assertion

I'd like to address the slur on Korean pilots of a certain generation as it demonstrates just how complex cultural influences can be and also how they can be tackled.

In his book, Outliers, Malcolm Gladwell describes how a whole series of Korean Air crashes in the early 1990s had an underlying cultural cause – which was the natural hierarchial deference of Korean society. (Their record was so bad US Army personnel were banned from flying with them in 1999 – you were something like 17 times more likely to die flying Korean Air than United Airlines at the time).

Analysis of the black box recordings found that crucially engineers and co-pilots would hint at concerns rather than telling the captain directly. (Perceived lack of due respect or could be met with a back handed slap). He describes the following example from a doomed flight that was already in great peril and in which hundreds of people died …

Co-pilot to pilot "don't you think it rains more, in this area?"

But meaning "Captain, you have committed us to a visual approach, with no back up plan (*an error caused by fatigue*), and the weather is terrible. You assume that we will break out of this cloud in time to see the runway. But what if we don't? It's pitch black, pouring with rain and the airports glide scope is out of order" (*mechanical failure of a device that wasn't essential normally but would have helped greatly in this situation*).

For this deference issue to result in tragedy they found that you need to add a small mechanical failure, bad weather and pilot fatigue too. However, they found that training all crew in assertion techniques and business English solved the problem. Korean airlines are now as safe as any other. Of course please see Chapter 12 on assertion and Chapter 2 on the 'cheese model' and 'breaking the chain'.

So in Summary - Is There Such a Thing as Accident Proneness? I hope I've made a case that adding *people* to the workplace is a minefield. (As if you didn't know!) But is there a generally accident prone personality? The short answer is that despite some recent controversy about the subject - yes there is. Of course there is.

However, it has to be stressed that outside of hugely safety critical tasks like flying fighter jets it's not really viable to use measures of these traits to influence the selection process. Far more important in most organisations is that focusing too much on the individual may well distract us from the bigger picture which is that *for the vast majority of tasks the environment and the culture (even the national culture!) is far more important in determining accidents than the person.* Most jobs are undertaken by average people and so any job should be designed in the first place to minimise the likelihood or problems caused by individual variation occurring in the first place and maximising the likelihood of any errors being spotted and quickly controlled when they do.

Though complex psychological assessment is beyond the resources of most companies we *can* take basic steps to ensure a decent fit between task and person. For most situations this will just involve task analysis and training. (Techniques of analysis covered in section two of the book). People are different in a 1001 different ways and even differ day to day and hour to hour. We just need to be aware of that when analysing incidents and *reacting* to issues. As ever, better than that, we should prepare for it *pro-actively*.

Ostriches and the HSE

"It is only when the tide goes out that you know who's been swimming naked"

Warren Buffet (World's Richest Man)

The trouble with putting a magnifying glass to what you find under the stone is that some management teams feel they are "doing the HSE's work for them". At one of our first user conferences on human factors this was raised as a serious concern and after some research with HSE direct we were able to announce that their basic position was as follows. (I paraphrase).

"It's true that if something goes wrong and you are subject to an investigation and you have files full of good analysis and improvement ideas that are easy to do and have not been done then those files make our job easy for us. However, this is not a worse position to be in that not doing the analysis in the first place and not even knowing what you need to do to improve … in fact in many respects it is better of course because you can demonstrate that some effort has been made. So the files help us – but we'd get to the same point in the end – it just would make our visit shorter…

As with everything in life, the temptation to keep your head down and 'get through today' makes life easier on a given day. It's just never very effective in the medium to long term. The next section describes the psychology of temptation in detail.

Summary of Main Points

- Behavioural approaches support and enhance other processes but are not a magic bullet.

- Good behavioural approaches are about analysis not blame.

- As such, a good behavioural approach can enhance any culture improvement approach regardless of a company's starting point.

- As ever, management commitment is the key to success.

CHAPTER 5

BEHAVIOURAL SAFETY

Comparing "Full" and "Top Down" Processes

At events about 'Proactive Safety' or 'Affective Safety Management' or even 'Energising Your Health and Safety Training' I am frequently asked practical questions about 'behavioural safety' and told 'finding out more about BBS is my main reason for being here'. That's understandable as it's very much where I specialised initially as a consultant and if you vaguely recognise the name it'll probably be as 'that chap who instigated the European Behavioural Safety User Conference'. Noting this trend I have therefore included a short strengths and weaknesses section on behavioural safety despite a suggestion that it rather goes off on a tangent.

A Simple Distinction

Very broadly, behavioural approaches can be categorised in several ways, with "top down" versus "bottom up" perhaps the most obvious. Both can take the form of either a short-term initiative or a long-term process.

Bottom up processes that involve both high levels of involvement and measurement are often more accurately called 'full' processes as they involve the workforce and management.

Essentially, however, every programme on the market incorporates one or more of six elements:

- Workforce Ownership and Involvement
- Root-cause analysis
- Behavioural Measurement
- Feedback (and Goal-Setting).
- Awareness Raising
- Management and Supervision.

You will see that there is a huge overlap with topics in this book with one exception. Feedback in this context might not just mean face-to-face communication but may also mean percentage behavioural scores on charts around the site and participative goal setting sessions where the workforce is told: "We are at 60% for housekeeping" and asked "What's a hard but realistic goal for us to achieve in the next three months?" The answer will of course be flagged on the charts, which will be updated perhaps weekly or monthly.

The "Full" Process

Building on academic research and the quality-focused work of Deming, Thomas Krause and others pioneered "full" behavioural safety commercially. Essentially, "full" behavioural safety processes attempt to incorporate all six pillars. Methodological variations abound and there is no "best way". A company should look at all the options before selecting the elements that best suit them. In summary, however, the full approach is as follows.

Summary of Basic "Full" Programme Methodology

Typically:

- A culture survey is undertaken and a gap analysis and action plan prepared.
- The senior management team attend a half-day workshop where the action plan is debated, tailored and resourced. (This tying the following into the formal appraisal system)
- All managers attend a behavioural safety leadership course.
- Awareness presentations are made to the whole workforce and volunteers are sought.
- Some of these then receive training to form a Steering Committee (SC). Other volunteers may be trained as Observers at a later date.
- The SC – if it decides it wants to run a "full" programme – then finalise the draft materials it has been provided with through consultation with colleagues. (i.e Behavioural check-sheets, awareness raising leaflets and the like)
- These measures are validated and then used to collect baseline data.
- Goals are set and scores are displayed on feedback charts.
- Underlying reasons (or "root-causes") for non-compliance are investigated and cost effective solutions identified and implemented.
- Additional benefits are derived from the mentoring benefits of one-to-one conversations – and the positive feedback contained in those conversations – and awareness raising designed by the workforce.

In advanced methodologies you might see the SC tailor a half-day awareness raising session around the key elements of behavioural safety (Break the chain and analysis is key etc), then provide two volunteers to be trained as in-house trainers. They will then deliver the half-day course to the whole workforce and seek additional volunteers.

Typical Strengths of 'Full' Programmes

- A higher level of ownership, which delivers several positive spin-offs.

- Better measurement as its peer-to-peer, so workers are more likely to act naturally and more bodies means a better sample (so better feedback on such as percentage feedback charts and the more accurate targeting of resources).

- Better root-cause analysis (as "no name, no blame" peer-to-peer conversations tend to produce more objective qualitative data).

- More credible awareness-raising campaigns (as the campaigns are designed and often delivered by the workforce themselves).

Combined this often gives dramatic and on-going improvement in safety standards. The CarePlus campaign on the Cormorant Alpha (see Kiel Institute report HSE Offshore Technology Report 2000/048) and the Murchsafer campaign on the Murchison (see Off Shore Step Change leaflet December 2001) are examples of this "full" approach. The behavioural safety case study in the IOSH publication "Promoting a positive culture" was also a full methodology.

Weaknesses

The major weakness is that it is more time consuming and may be a more radical adjustment for all concerned. (See notes on the management of change above). Certainly, a more substantial "culture" change may be required regarding levels of trust and autonomy. Consequently there is a greater strain on management commitment levels because of the above but also because improved communication means managers need to respond to ideas if the credibility of the process is not to be compromised. They first need to find the time for the workforce to run the process. Then they need to find the money and time to action virtually all ideas that are demonstrably "high impact low cost" as well as deciding within an agreed time frame what to do with the "high impact high cost" suggestions.

This second point is of course true of any approach. It is just that an approach with high levels of ownership generates relatively more suggestions.

The "Top Down" Approach

Many companies tackle safety behaviour with almost entirely supervisor-led programmes that have a behavioural focus. There are a large number of these but the underlying approach is that they are largely management driven. (These programmes/ initiatives are often tailored by an organisation following some consultation with the workforce and/or its representatives). Frequently, however, workforce involvement is often largely compulsory and any data collected through opportunity audits.

There are many variations on this approach and some are so close to 'standard management' that they shouldn't really qualify as 'behavioural safety' at all. For example, despite being included in some overview studies of 'behavioural approaches' initiatives such as "Time Out for Safety" (TOFS) are not really behavioural safety at all, but are rather a practical, sensible and high profile encouragement to apply the basic principles of good safety management.

The Overlap with "Full" Programmes

The overlap with full programmes is that:

- Both focus on reducing unsafe behaviours or unsafe conditions that are hard evidence of behaviour

- Both seek to raise awareness of behavioural items

That is, they are following the principles of Heinrich's Triangle. In addition:

- Both stress the importance of supervision and management

- The better top-down programmes also focus on root-cause analysis as well as the approach of "follow the rules – they're there for a reason"

- Hard data may also be collected but, frankly, is often of limited use. (See notes on lead indicators above)

Strengths

The great strength of these is that they:

- fit well with existing management systems

- stress the importance of line management influencing and "modelling" safety on a day-to-day basis

- are also relatively easy to undertake as they can be incorporated into a daily site tour.

Weaknesses

Their major weakness is perhaps that they can be seen as patronising if not done well and deliver little, if any, front-line "ownership". Though for ideological reasons I must admit a bias towards the 'full' approach it must be admitted that all the weaknesses detailed below can well apply to them too. It's just that because of higher levels of involvement and ownership they seem to appear less often. Regardless you may see that these approaches:

- Lead to confrontation and defensiveness. (Particularly as, typically, the person observing or leading the observation team will also have a responsibility for discipline)

- May lead to "tit for tat" retaliation – or, alternatively "back scratching" style Mexican stand-offs

- May lead cards to be completed over a coffee (from memory or even from imagination)

- Usually involve people talking to workers only about subjects they are comfortable with

- Involve observation tours at times that are not always stratified (always on a Friday afternoon for example, giving a skewed view of safety)

- (Consequently) rarely provide accurate percentage data. Cards given out can be counted but while these "head count opportunity" samples can produce interesting looking pie charts, they should not be confused with scientific sampling techniques

- Finally, they do not set the best possible situation for root-cause analysis as operatives approached often report themselves defensive and wary.

There is absolutely no reason why the above weaknesses have to be seen. Certainly, if you took the blurb on the outside of the box at face value you'd be convinced you'd get all the benefits for limited disruption. Having undertaken numerous audits of such systems, however, I can state that you very often find most, or all, of this list to be true. Sadly, though I much prefer the full approach as an ideology we find that most of the negatives listed there are true too.

Reflecting this, "Affective Safety Management" is quite explicitly an attempt to find some middle ground and maximise effectiveness whilst minimizing inconvenience!

"Advanced Behavioural Safety"

You may have come across the term 'Advanced Behavioural Safety'. For a while in early 2007, it looked very much like it would be the 'next big thing'. It still might so it's worth briefly addressing. The versions I have seen focus squarely on the individual and utilise a discovered learning / coaching / NLP style of discussing safety with an individual and getting them to fully appreciate the risks they are running. Basically, this is a more in-depth way of approaching the "what's the worst that could happen?" style of questioning. The aim is that the person's mindset is changed from 'this will be OK' to 'this could end badly'.

The strength of this approach is that it, of course, links to the sections in this book on 'Heinrich and the chain', 'behavioural root-cause analysis' (or at least the individual perception of 'pay off' element of this), 'coaching' and 'advanced training for active learning'. So in many respects it's all good stuff. The downside is the very valid one that is levelled at all person centred approaches to safety. That is that it's too focused on the person and not focused enough on the environment. In this it echoes perhaps the key learning point from the Baker Report: "Don't forget the basics".

Summary of Main Points

- Anything that seeks to focus systematically on reducing unsafe behaviour is a behavioural approach.

- Because the focus in on people's behaviour it can backfire if done clumsily.

- The more complicated approaches can be more effective as they utilize more tools

- But that, of course, makes them more difficult to implement and requires more management commitment.

SECTION 2

APPLICATION OF AFFECTIVE
SAFETY MANAGEMENT

CHAPTER 6

CONTEXT OF AFFECTIVE SAFETY MANAGEMENT

In the introduction we suggested that in essence ASM is:

- *Get out there and lead from the front... (because)*
- *Any risk is too much risk as it mounts up quickly ... (so)*
- *Focus on and challenge day to day issues as well as the 'big' stuff ... (by)*
- *Asking the right questions in the right way... (so that you can)*
- *Always analyse intelligently before you act... (and when you act remember)*
- *The best coaches only lose their temper and throw things occasionally...*

Previous chapters have essentially striven to make the case as to why companies should do this. The chapters that follow from here attempt to summarise how to do this effectively.

This chapter starts with a consideration of some contextual issues that straddle both theory and practise. These are organisational change and a brief consideration of values and priorities. It then considers five of the six behaviour clusters that distinguish pro-active companies from merely compliant ones. The sixth factor, communication, fits better in a later chapter on interpersonal influencing skills.

Organisational Change

At training events we get a volunteer strapped up to a heart monitor similar to those used in the gym and call them to the front just before we discuss organisational change. We try and pressurise them by asking for a song or an embarrassing memory ... then stop them quickly and check the heart rate. Usually it will be around 120 when it was around 65 to 70 when they were seated.

If something in the environment worries us then we respond instinctively, and change is a worry. Another exercise is to ask delegates to list 10 reasons to open a bottle of champagne and the responses will include "birth of a child!", "getting married!", "moving house!", "a promotion!", "a lottery win!" and of course "getting divorced!". All of these things also appear on another list – the 'top ten most stressful things'. The common denominator is change ... basically people are hard wired to dislike it, though obviously some dislike it more than others. It goes back to the days when we lived in caves, foraging for a living and living on the edge – where any extra effort might be fatal. So we come across a new animal or a new bush and instead of being able to shout "oh goody, a cow near a strawberry bush!" and get stuck in - we have to worry about whether we are about to get eaten or poisoned.

The point is the very simple one that changing anything requires a strategy that takes into account the fact that most workers and sometimes managers will kick against it instinctively – even if it's genuinely for the better. So despite the many and varied benefits of "affective safety" half the workforce will say the new approach is "logistically impossible" and the other half will say it's both impossible and misguided. Or to quote the oft used expression "what's this crap now exactly?!"

One of the core values of a proactive company is that it understands that if it isn't actively moving forwards then it's probably drifting backwards. Being comfortable with change and evolution in general is something all companies should strive for. Clearly, the consultation, communication and analysis approach advocated here is entirely congruent with doing this well.

There are thousands of excellent textbooks on the subject but perhaps the biggest selling management book of recent years – "Who Moved my Cheese" – sums it up very well. It is essentially a parable about two mice, one who realises early on that the cheese is running out and seeks out a new source, and the other who doesn't give it much thought until it does. Basically he starves and the moral of the book is essentially:

Change is inevitable – those who embrace it and make the most of it will flourish, those who try and pretend it's not happening will struggle.

I always carry this book (and a copy of its satirical follow up) to conferences with me so I can whip out the follow up book and say "I prefer this one though – 'I moved your sodding cheese!'"

Core Values and Priorities

It is worth stressing a key difference between priorities and core values. I'll try and quote as close to verbatim as memory allows an observation made to me by an experienced and knowledgeable safety practitioner that's always stuck with me and refers directly to the 'safety wave' principle discussed above.

"Core values are deeply embedded and fundamental to the way a company operates at all times. Priorities change and are the sort of thing politicians bang on about. I'm not often convinced by the politicians and when I see companies saying 'safety is our number one priority' I'm not often convinced by them either".

If nothing else it's a very good starting point for a debate. What do you think?

Organisational Values and Beliefs

Given that the 'who moved my cheese?' principle of embracing change in order to flourish is true it's essential that an organisation 'lives' this proactive approach on a day-to-day basis. As well as 'if we can't articulate how we're going forward and actively improving, we're probably going backwards', some other key principles are:

- Good safety is good business – we don't spend on safety, we invest
- Good safety is something that everyone has to embrace themselves
- It is not something that's done to you or for you
- So everyone has to be actively involved and it has to start with the board
- It must be lead with the workforce by line management.

It is of course impossible to put these principles into action without high levels of senior management commitment translated into a sound high level strategy and planning. However, addressing such issues in detail is well beyond the scope of this book. (This assumes of course that the reader is in an organisation that is broadly calculative and is primarily interested in the nuts and bolts of moving forward). The rest of this booklet therefore tries to detail what a proactive culture looks like on a day-to-day basis.

As briefly introduced above, it has been found that essentially a proactive culture has six sets of behaviour that distinguish it from a compliant culture either because the management do them or because management does them well. I'll try and define specifically what we mean by well as we go. As a reminder these are:

- Behavioural Analysis
- Modelling
- Challenging
- Involving the workforce
- Lead measurement
- Communication.

Summary of Main Points

- Change is inevitable and essential for an improvement in safety culture. Companies have to manage it and ideally learn to embrace it.
- Safety needs to be a core value – not this year's priority.

CHAPTER 7

ROOT-CAUSE ANALYSIS AND JUST CULTURE

At the inquiry into the Columbia space shuttle disaster, the chairwoman of the mission management team was asked what she did about dissenting opinions and she replied that when they heard about them she took them on board etc.

Then she was asked "but sometimes of course they are out there and you don't get to hear about them... what do you do to go out and find them?"

(A now infamous) silence...

This section is about **proactive** analysis.

Human Error

This is clearly a huge area of work and research and this section merely aims to give an overview of the main principles and categorisations for contextual purposes. The basic point is that human error is inevitable – but more inevitable in some circumstances than others.

The basic dichotomy is that risky behaviour can be either classed as intentional or unintentional. If it is intentional then some form of behavioural analysis will be required as is described in this section. (For example, is it because of the person thinking they know best or are they trying to 'please' the company?) If it's unintentional then it takes us to the field of human error analysis – and there are many types of human error analysis tools and categorisations that can be used.

Broadly, however, the error might be caused by:

- Perception
- Memory
- Mental Processing
- Physical Action

These can be influenced by such factors as fatigue, health, fitness, stress and the ergonomic design of the task and so on.

Imagine a dinner guest is late and the phone rings.

> It is your guest. Your friend really shouldn't talk on the phone whilst driving but does – and he has a habit of discussing complicated business issues as he drives. He has got hopelessly distracted and driven straight past the exit he needed. It is 12 miles to the next one and traffic is heavy. (Among other things – and we'll get back to that – a mental processing error).

Your friend rings back 30 minutes later.

He was back on track but was convinced he knew the way from the motorway.

His memory for such things is usually perfect … or so he says.

He also forgot to bring a map with him … now he's hopelessly lost and will be even later. (A memory error – though his wife, sitting next to him, is overheard in the background calling it something else!)

Your friend rings back 30 minutes later.

He came across a sharp corner that's badly signposted and badly lit – he couldn't read it so he only realised too late that he needed to turn sharply (he's needed glasses for years but is too vain and stubborn to get them). In having to break sharply he put the car into a skid into the ditch. The car is drivable but he'll be even later – he's waiting for the RAC to come and tow him out. (This is – mostly at the point of incident anyway – a perception error).

Your friend rings back 30 minutes later.

He was rushing to make up time and has taken a (perfectly straightforward) corner far too quickly. He's lost control and put his car through a hedge and into a field just down the road … could you please go and pick him up? (Arguably this is a good old fashioned action error).

It will be obvious that these categories interlink and overlap of course. You might well argue that getting distracted and forgetting to turn off at the right junction is in some respects a memory problem or that failing to get his eyes checked is a decision making problem. Choosing to use his phone in the car could of course be described as a decision error as well as a distraction … and so on.

The police ring.

You're friend won't be coming at all. His wife has beaten him half to death with a tyre jack. You note to yourself that this isn't an unintentional slip or mistake but better categorised as a "conscious and intentional violation!"

Regardless of categorisation the main thrust of proactive human error work is to ensure that the organisation doesn't put a worker – or allow them to put themselves – in a position where human error is more likely. The most obvious overlap and interlink here is with Behavioural Root-cause Analysis.

A summary of the whole ergonomic/ human factors field is that it aims to:

- Minimize the likelihood of an error occurring
- Minimise the time required to spot that error
- Minimise the time and effort required to recover from that error.

"We're building this ship all wrong". Some time ago I was with a ship building client in the Middle East and we worked through some of the themes in this chapter. At the end of the day they were in a huddle talking in an animated fashion. I asked them if everything was OK and was told "well after a fashion… we've been musing on what you've been telling us and do you know what? We're building this ship all wrong … we should never have agreed to build it like this.

Behavioural Root-Cause Analysis & the "Fundamental Attribution Error"

I have an ex-army friend who runs 'executive stretch' courses for companies. He's single, looks a bit like Hugh Grant and you can imagine used to meet a lot of women this way. However, he has now stopped dating delegates he meets on these courses. He explains that 'on the course with all the action and adventure and excitement and me barking orders and dashing about in my uniform and so on … but when I walk into the pub or restaurant to meet them after in my civvies I can see their face drop … it's just not the same'.

He's describing a very well researched psychological phenomenon called the "fundamental attribution error" which is that we all typically give too much weight to the person and not enough to the environment when assessing a situation. In Elvis's words it's very difficult to "walk a mile in a man's shoes before we judge."

Importantly from a 'blame/ just culture' perspective this is particularly true when something has gone wrong. For example, have you ever punched a wardrobe door when it's caught you painfully on the knee? You now have a sore hand as well as a sore knee – but the dead tree remains pretty impassive I've found.

This section is all about techniques that mitigate the instinctive impact of that instinctive error.

A Root-cause Analysis Exercise

Please complete the following questionnaire. It's one which is one we like to read out at live events. Have you ever been guilty of:

- Drinking your weekly allowance of alcohol in a single 24 hour session?

- Smoking?

- Taking a drug not prescribed by a doctor?

- Making a resolute resolution because you want to be the sort of grandparent that can play touch rugby with your grandchildren, so it's improved diet, less alcohol, stretching exercises and yoga and regular visits to the gym. And really meaning it... but it's all out of the window in weeks?

- Driving at 50% above the speed limit (so 75 in a 50; 45 in a 30 and so on)?

- Driving through a traffic light as it turns from amber to red?

- Driving when you think you're under the drink drive limit but you're not entirely certain and would worry if breathalysed?

- Driving when you know you're not under the limit?

- Having unprotected sex with someone in the past 15 years even though you've little or no idea where they have been or who with – but they look kind of wholesome so it'll probably be ok?

- Having any sort of sex, protected or otherwise with someone other than the partner who would be very upset if they found out?

At conferences we'll often get someone young in the front row shout out "house!" at the end of this list and add "and last week … living on the edge me!" Most people, up to and including Presidents fail and often pretty miserably. We all know there are risks associated with these behaviours but they tend to be long term and uncertain so we tend to get on with things and let the future take care of itself. The trouble is the future isn't always rosy...

Oscar Wilde said he could resist anything but temptation and Stephen Fry jokes that what he does with temptation is to yield to it straight away as it "saves time on faffing about". This resonates for most but in a calculative (i.e compliance based) safety culture we pretty much ignore this truism and assume that people become rational, long term and logical when they enter the workplace. When something goes wrong we ask "what were you doing?", "didn't you realise the risks you were running?", "how could you have been so foolish to take the risk?"

But people don't change personality when they come to work and if there are temptations to take risks because the safe way is slow, uncomfortable or inconvenient then it's just a question of how many will cut corners and how often.

Perhaps the golden rule of Affective safety is if someone is taking a risk – first ask why before you make any sort of judgment or response. (Except when there is an immediate risk, of course, where the response needs to be "stop!") Further, a behavioural approach to root-cause analysis always assumes that, in the majority of cases, unsafe behaviours occur for a reason that makes sense to the individual at the time. In particular we need to consider the immediate consequences of the behaviour.

A fundamental principle of most safety management is that we are long term, rational and logical in our thinking – but just like with smoking, speeding, diet and most New Year resolutions as above we respond frequently to rewards or consequences that are:

- soon
- certain and (at the time)
- positive

Consequently, companies have found that designing out temptations proves far more effective than increasing punitive action – especially because design solutions are permanent. Therefore the comment "I can't be bothered" or "it's too time consuming" should be understood as "some people are tempted not to do X because it is inconvenient. However, we can make it more convenient by ...". What companies often find is that making the safe way as quick, comfortable and convenient as the unsafe way is a very cost effective and adult way of improving safety behaviour.

Certainly, many "obvious" –and practical and cost effective – design solutions have been elicited through a systematic evaluation of the antecedents and consequences of an unsafe behaviour or condition.

Technique One - Behavioural Root-cause Analysis (ABC)

This behavioural root-cause analysis technique is sometimes referred to as "ABC analysis" - with ABC standing for Antecedents, Behaviours and Consequences. There is not space in this book for really detailed notes on the approach – but it is covered in great detail in the freely available 2002 HSE research publication "Strategies to Improve Safe Behaviour". Briefly, however the approach is to:

- Identify the unsafe behaviour and its safe counterpart
- Make a list of all the antecedents (i.e triggers and relevant contextual issues) to both those behaviours. (For example, warning signs, training, rules, the need for a piece of PPE , or perhaps the worker was hungover or drunk)

- Make a list of all the potential consequences of unsafe and safe behaviours. (For example, speed, comfort, increased risk, decreased risk)

- Look in particular for consequences that are soon, certain and positive. Then change the design of the job or task to ensure the consequences for safe behaviour are at least as powerful as those for unsafe behaviour – or just use praise of safe behaviour as a soon, certain and positive consequence.

The Rationale

By listing the Triggers/ Antecedents systematically we often suggest a creative engineering solution that would otherwise have been missed had we jumped straight to some "obvious" solutions. This is because "if you solved a problem with a hammer last week … this week everything looks like a nail" to paraphrase James Reason.

In addition, "scoring" the consequences helps us concentrate on the "heat" (or temptation) in the relationship, and helps us identify high and low impact solutions as we know a high impact solution has to address the temptation directly. If it doesn't, then it isn't high impact. For example, knowing you will be fired if caught committing a certain unsafe act only reduces temptation but does not entirely design it out. Making the unsafe act impossible or more trouble than the unsafe way reduces the temptation.

Technique Two – Five Why's Analysis

There is a famous play called 'six degrees of separation' which is based on the premise that we are all connected to everyone else on the planet in no more than six steps. For example, to my partner's delight I can make it to George Clooney in just three. An old school-friend of mine (Jeremy Thomas) married the actress Drew Barrymore (briefly, in the mid 1990s) and she has met George Clooney many times.

The same principle works with safety: if you keep asking the question "why?", You should get to the real root-cause of a problem in five or six steps maximum. Now it could, as above, be less – or it might be six. Often, there will obviously be more than one answer and the trick is to map the thing out. Usually it'll branch out and then come back into two or three key points.

We have an exercise where we ask if anyone has been burgled or had their car broken into recently. We ask "how did you feel about that?" and write the answer on a flip chart along with the answer to "what did that make you want to do?" Of course torture features frequently. We then ask delegates to 'five why's' youth crime in the UK and they work through issues like lack of money, drug addiction, poor parenting and poor schooling, and branch out into unlikely to get caught, punishment, no deterrent and so on until they (invariably) present back something thoughtful, comprehensive, progressive and practical that might have come straight from a Labour party think tank called "tough on crime and tough on the causes of crime".

We point out that this is a long way in terms of depth and long-term sustainability from their initial and instinctive "beat them half to death". The analogy with the rushed, exasperated and 'blaming' supervisor is very easy to make.

Five Why's and A B C – A Simple but Tragic Case Study

I was involved in a fatality investigation in Glasgow many years ago. A workman had been crushed to death by a two ton slab of metal in a hole in the ground. The safe system of work was for him to secure it at the top with a colleague then secure it at the bottom. They chose to do both simultaneously – and it slipped and killed the chap in the bottom of the hole. Why was he tempted to cut a corner like this? Because they wanted to save time and get themselves to the pub to watch the football. Celtic and Rangers were playing that day. Why were they able to do this? Because the supervisor had gone on ahead to get the beers in and secure a good table and had left them to "job and knock" (i.e. follow him on as soon as they had finished).

He'd presented them with a classic temptation and, as stated above, we too often yield to temptations. Just as the base of Heinrich's triangle is full of unsafe acts and conditions, it should also be considered to be full of temptations.

The more temptations to cut corners, the bigger the top of the triangle.

Lack of Root-Cause Analysis

Therefore any "root-cause analysis" process must seek to ask objectively "why" an event has occurred : the lower down Heinrich's Triangle this question is asked then basically the more proactive the methodology.

Certainly, when reviewing existing safety systems and behavioural safety systems one of the biggest problems identified is that there is too much emphasis on "symptoms" and not enough on root causes. Consequently we often find:

- Time and effort spent enforcing rules and regulations that are impractical or contradictory

- The admonishment of employees who are honestly trying their best. (And who subsequently very much resent being "unfairly told off")

- "Crap lists" that although they are diligently circulated and rectified simply recur time after time.

Basically once you fully understand the ABC principle it clarifies why so many "standard" responses are so ineffective. For example, pick up any Accident Investigation file and you're likely to find something close to the following:

"TM did something he wasn't supposed to do and consequently suffered a minor injury. We've disciplined him for that and proactively sent a memo round reminding people never to do this act".

Clearly there is no analysis as to why the act occurred and putting the buzz word 'proactive' in the sentence doesn't make sending a memo around any more effective!

Enhancing Root-Cause Analysis

There are several ways of enhancing the daily root-cause analysis of unsafe acts and conditions:

- By introducing a workforce run element to the investigation process. Experience shows that more honest and open responses are generated where colleagues talk to colleagues in a credible 'no name, no blame' way

- Training all key personnel – by which we mean all managers, supervisors, safety professionals, safety reps and any shop floor volunteers - in basic root-cause analysis techniques

- Training key personnel in basic interview skills and listening techniques (For example the use of neutral and hypothetical questions).

Hypothetical questions you can ask include:

* If you really had to, how could you work more quickly?

* What's uncomfortable about working safely?

* Are there any aspects of working safely that slow down the job?

* What's inconvenient about working safely?

* Any aspects of working safely that make you feel silly or foolish because you are or would be in the minority?

The important thing is that the information contained in the answers to these questions will be just as useful as admissions and confessions. When undertaking root-cause analysis it's not a confession we want, it's information!

In addition it might be useful to:

Train key personnel volunteers in basic assertion and communication techniques so that they can avoid putting the interviewee on the defensive and can best deal with the "awkward" customer. Experience shows that using these techniques is applicable even if the person is to be formally admonished in some way – indeed building in an opportunity to show their knowledge will probably be welcome to someone who has just been pulled up and reprimanded.

Effective Root-Cause Analysis and the Supervision of Safety. (An additional benefit)

Companies find that the "active" supervision of safety is enhanced by transparently being seen striving hard to design out environmental factors that increase temptation. In addition, because incisive root-cause analysis is so effective the number of transgressions will reduce greatly. Those that continue to transgress stand out more and are more likely to be genuinely guilty of an irresponsible act. Any negative consequence is therefore seen as more legitimate.

Summary of Main Points

- Human Error is inevitable and we need proactively to look to predict it and manage it.

- If an unsafe behaviour has a soon, certain and positive consequence, people will be tempted to cut corners.

- With these temptations to cut corners – where employees CAN act safely but it's inconvenient or uncomfortable – it's just a question of how many people will give in and how often. So again we need to proactively predict it and manage it.

- If you can meaningfully ask the question "why?" about an incident or behaviour at any time, but fail to ask it, any action you undertake may well be addressing a symptom and not a root cause.

- The question "what's slow, uncomfortable or inconvenient about doing this job safely?" is pretty much "what corners do you cut when I'm not about?" but with better answers and less negative impact.

CHAPTER 8

WORKFORCE INVOLVEMENT

Modelling

This is a very short section. Above we have described how a safe behaviour that is 50:50 gives a worker free choice as to whether they comply or not. But when it comes to managers – who are, de facto, all key safety leaders whether they like it or not – it is even simpler. A safety leader who cuts even a single corner – whatever the reason – automatically undermines the whole process because their actions speak volumes. What such an action says is:

"this behaviour is highly desirable but not always essential ... there are times when cutting this corner is acceptable".

I was escorted around a factory in Italy once by the head of safety who himself wasn't wearing his mandatory PPE or keeping to the prescribed walkways. When I commented on it he said "I don't need to, I know all the risks...".

'Do as I say not as I do' doesn't even work with a five-year-old.

A more subtle example involves the current Prime Minister, Gordon Brown. He was visiting a ship yard to launch a ship just before becoming PM and was handed all the required PPE. He donned the hat, boots and coveralls but handed back the safety glasses commenting "I only have one eye and the other one doesn't work very well. If these aren't prescription glasses – and I can see they aren't – then I'll not be able to see anything.

The management team held a quick emergency meeting and agreed that people would understand – after all there wasn't any real work being undertaken on the day and risk was minimal. The MD who chaired the meeting (Vic) says now "if I could turn the bloody clock back I would... every weekly meeting and tool box talk – and particularly every disciplinary ... "what about Gordon Brown?!" I've been paying for that decision for years now!".

We talked before about the fabled "tipping point" being about 85 to 90% with peers. You might argue that with management it works in the other direction and the tipping point starts at 99%!

Challenging

This is another quite short entry, though the next section is essentially all about how to challenge well. To briefly consider whether to challenge at all ... a simple truism.

"If you walk past an unsafe act or condition you leave the risk present on the day itself and, worse than that, you condone it for the future".

In world class safety cultures, managers always model safety and make sure they frequently challenge the little things too. I attended a talk once by a construction worker who described how he noticed a badly guarded hole when making his way to the canteen 'for a quick brew'. He noted that a dip in the ground made it quite difficult to see and thought to stop and discuss it with the workmen nearby who seemed to have moved on to another task but then he thought he'd address it on his way back as frankly he was "gasping". He never finished his coffee because of the commotion that broke out outside. He said that he wasn't exaggerating for effect and that the man who was killed that day really was his best friend. It's said that the highest standard you can expect is the lowest standard that you will tolerate.

A client that made bulldozers had a notoriously bullish client who had the habit of walking straight on to site to check on work. He made these visits in his suit and brogues and nothing else - certainly not the required PPE. One day someone challenged him and got a right mouthful in return. Worse, the client marched straight to the manager's office to complain. The manager backed the worker and commented that in fact he'd be seeking him out later to commend him. At this point the client blew a fuse and stormed out slamming the door and threatening to pull the contract. Our management hero here (Jason) confessed to a sleepless night but when the client came back the next day he was a bit sheepish ... and apologised. He now always wears the required PPE.

Kitty Genovese and the Bystander Effect. Kitty Genovese was a young woman who was murdered in Queens New York in 1964. She was attacked outside the flats in which she lived and dozens of people heard the attack but no-one called the police or intervened. They all assumed someone else would. Twenty minutes later the attacker returned to rob, stab and rape her a second time but again no one called the police until it was too late.

The media coverage horrified New Yorkers and it helped inspire some famous research into the "bystander effect". The classic experiment is to have a line of people select which is the shortest of a number of lines and the trick is that though the task is quite difficult success should be about 100%. The trick is to place a stooge somewhere towards the end of a line of say 10 people with the others all briefed to lie and to choose the shortest but one. 90% of the time the stooge (9th in the line of 10) will lie and agree with the others. Interestingly, if just one person is allowed to call it truthfully then this drops to just 10%. (Similar experiments have been done with smoke seeping into a room and the stooge sitting there until the room is dangerously full and the experiment needs to be stopped).

More interestingly for the world of safety is the finding that after a 15 minute tutorial on the bystander effect people are something like 3 times more likely to be the first to say something and intervene – usually followed by several others all saying "I was about to say that/ do that myself!".

I'd like to suggest that everyone should get that 15 minute tutorial!

Workforce Involvement and "Cognitive Dissonance"

Research has shown that not only do you smile more if you're happy but that it works the other way around. You will feel happier if you force yourself to smile – and jokes told to you when you're holding a pencil in your teeth (forcing a 'smile') will be rated funnier. There is an interesting relationship between behaviour and attitudes.

On a more subtle level a famous research study bribed people to vote against their choice of candidate either with a big bribe or a little bribe. Then they asked people how well disposed they were to the candidate they had been bribed to vote for. They found no shift where the bribe was big but a small but significant shift where the bribe was small. A phenomenon called cognitive dissonance explains this. Basically, we like our actions and our values to be in line … if they aren't, we are psychologically uncomfortable. The big bribe meant an overwhelming reason so they did it and dismissed it. However, the little bribe made them less comfortable – so much so that it actually shifted their perception of the candidate.

We can often deal with this discomfort with a quick bit of self-serving justification. For example, we might admit that we do drive when close to the drink drive limit even though we've seen the research and know that, though technically legal, we're twice as likely to crash – but it doesn't mean we're not safety conscious and responsible (a self image we value) because we compensate by "concentrating twice as hard!" Obviously that's how we get through the day a lot of the time – and self serving rationalisations abound in the media. Yesterday a famous model claimed she was arrested (again) not because she'd behaved badly (yet again) but because she was black. There's the ex-wife of a famous musician who didn't want details of the case published not because the judge accused her of bad behaviour, materialism and telling falsehoods but because she wanted to protect the privacy of her child.

However, most of us do change our behaviour to fit our beliefs when we realise they aren't congruent. More interesting in some ways is that we often change our beliefs to fit our behaviour. The 'small bribe' example above is a good example – and it has obvious implications for safety management.

Cults pray on this principle all the time. They never ask "will you give us all your money and give up your family and friends?"; they ask "can you spare five minutes to fill in this questionnaire?" Then "can you spare 10 minutes to talk to this kind looking chap about the results?" … and before you know it you've spent quite a lot of time on this and with these people and rather than admit that you've been gullible and the time spent has been wasted you throw good time after bad. On a more positive note if you can get someone to spend some time working for safety there is a good chance they will become more safety conscious. For example, the hard working line manager who carries out a safety contact conscientiously should automatically become more safety conscious.

At a safety awareness presentation – especially if it involves a high impact emotional content – people are often asked to stand up and promise to do "just one thing" more safely. If they make this promise with any degree of sincerity then the public nature of the promise means it is more likely to be kept; it is even better if this public promise is voluntary – because if the person chooses to stand up and make a public promise then it is highly likely to be kept.

So for example, they find themselves counting to ten and dropping back from someone who has cut them up on a motorway, instead of tailing them aggressively because they publicly said that such a response would make their children losing their father in a car accident far more likely – and they consider themselves a loving father. The latter is something they have no problem admitting publicly – even in front of the macho crew that make up B shift. But at a subconscious level a little voice is saying as they drop back "loving and mature and safety conscious".

Now clearly this is all getting a bit Freudian! However, the point was made above that changing people's attitudes through awareness raising alone is very difficult – they are all 'fine already thank you'. This makes it all the more important to harness this subconscious internal alignment process by getting people more involved in safety on a day-to-day basis.

Harnessing the Power of Choice

In one of his recent novels the English football enthusiast Nick Hornby describes a phenomenon about Scottish football fans. Please bear with me – the story does have considerable implications for a safety culture improvement! The conundrum is this – why do Scottish fans behave so well abroad when they didn't used to (think Wembley!) and don't necessarily in Glasgow now after a club game?

The answer is that at a World Cup some time ago the Scottish team were knocked out by the odd goal in a great game against the favourites, Brazil. Honour was satisfied and the papers were full the next day of pictures of men in kilts dancing good naturedly in fountains with pretty Brazilian women. The headlines were broadly 'Scots party after heroic exit… hardly any arrests… what a contrast with the English!' Ever since, Scots football fans have made an effort to behave well when abroad to show up the English! (Well this example was an excellent one up until Manchester council controversially encouraged tens of thousands of Rangers fans without tickets to come south for the UEFA cup final in 2008!)

The learning point is that it's difficult to overestimate how contrary people can be and that almost the worst way to get them to change is to tell them to. However, if they decide themselves that they want to change then things can be very different. Also, "discovered learning" training techniques focus squarely on this phenomenon and underpin much of the people-focused training required for a move to a proactive safety culture.

Increasing Workforce Ownership of Safety

The use of any of the above techniques and principles of analysis and adult-to-adult communications will help develop trust and safety motivation in the workforce. However, one theme stands out from all others in the research we have undertaken and that is that ownership primarily comes through choice – which is where the story of the Scottish football fans comes in. Because they chose to be "good" they were able to transform their behaviour abroad.

Choice isn't just about a quick consultation of a pre-made decision with the 'usual suspects'. This is because although in many respects ownership and consultation look similar they aren't and they deliver vastly different results in practice. To use another sporting analogy: a rugby scrum inching forwards or backwards looks very much the same from the stand – but if you're the scrum half who has to pick up the ball and do something with it, it makes all the difference in the world.

The biggest problem we see in this area is companies making decisions that are routinely ratified in a quick and meaningless consultation with the 'usual suspects' – or perhaps with a handful of hand-picked keen employees who tend to act very safely at all times (and so are atypical). Symptoms of this are numerous conversations over coffee or beer among workers saying "it's bleeding obvious that wouldn't work... if they'd asked me I'd have explained why to them ..." Or worse than that and in response to a "why didn't you say something?" jibe ... "actually I did try to mention it but no-one was listening".

Opportunities to devolve genuine choice include:

- What behaviours should we look at?
- What photographs best illustrate an acceptable standard?
- Running the ABC analysis and having full control of generating and labelling suggestions

If a full behavioural safety process has been introduced, as already described:

- Would you like to volunteer for training?

- What shall we call it?

- Shall we have a logo competition and if so which entry wins?

- Shall we try and generate lead data?

- (If yes) What shall we do with that lead data? Feedback charts? Goal-setting sessions?

So in summary ownership and consultation look similar at a glance but are radically different when you examine them closely. Ownership is about spreading choice about day-to-day behaviours and issues to as many of the workforce as possible.

A case study will help illustrate the issue. We were commissioned to run a behavioural programme on a ship being turned from an oil tanker to a floating oil platform at a Newcastle shipyard. We had volunteers who were trained up and who gave themselves a name and who had selected 20 behaviours to look at – i.e. to measure and analyse. They then ran a "we have a name, now we need a logo" competition - with the prize they suggested for the winning entry being a weekend for two in Amsterdam. Naturally, this generated plenty of entries – but the workforce was 2,000 strong and the vast majority totally ignored the whole thing.

However, it was noticed that 12 entries had come from children and it was suggested that these be turned into a calendar and offered to the workforce. Further, that all the children that entered should be given a Smiths "starter paint kit". This made for a excellent but inexpensive gift. The suggestions from children turned out to be inspired and suddenly the whole process took off – the calendar needed to be reprinted several times and the behavioural safety observers were generally greeted warmly rather than with scepticism. The bottom line was that despite the sheer scale and intensity of the work-scope we were able to run incident free until launch.

Sometimes the fact that the devil is in the little details works for you, and the people who do the job are easily the best placed to know what those little details are.

Safety Lead Indicators

There are any number of lead indicators that a company can use. These will typically focus on the effectiveness of implementation of a safety system and might include:

- Percentage of a safety management system that is compliant with current guidance (e.g. HS(G)65; BS 8800; OHSAS18001)
- Number of performed safety visits compared to the number planned.
- This section focuses briefly on behavioural lead indicators.
- Percentage of planned safety training achieved.
- The average time to action and implement any valid complaints or suggestions.

In addition, of course, a percentage measure of anything to do with such things as risk and hazard assessment or other control measures. This brief section covers behavioural lead measures and, following on from the section that says behavioural root-cause analysis is king, a description of my favourite lead measure that's less obvious than 'how many men have their hard hats on?'

Behavioural Lead Indicators

As a favour a journalist friend once smuggled me into the press box at a premiership deciding match. My job was to diligently note the time of all fouls, corners and shots – and note the player's name if I could. I was happy to help him like that for prime seats about 10 feet from where Posh Spice was sitting. Sadly the wrong team won because Patrick Vierra had a blinder. At the end of the game my friend just threw my notes away! Then he explained as I complained "ah, sorry about that but I needed you to look like you were working ... and not get totally caught up in the game!"

Basically behavioural lead indicators are measures of everyday behavioural acts and conditions at the bottom of Heinrich's classic Triangle. In this case corners and fouls – not goals and players being sent off.

Behavioural lead indicators do two things only. First they can deliver the benefit of "what gets measured gets done" and second they can deliver the benefits of "if you can measure it you can manage it". The latter is far more difficult than most companies appreciate, but for the former, you just need to be there making notes: the use of a good sample is sufficient to deliver the benefits of "what gets measured gets done" regardless of the quality of the data. In essence all you have to do is follow the ASM approach of getting out frequently and observing at busy times – and take a clipboard as you go.

However, you need accurate lead indicators to realise the benefits of "if we can measure it we can manage it". It must be stressed though that at the very least companies need to implement a process of actively monitoring behaviours with a good sample strategy to achieve the benefit of either , and developing accurate percentage measures takes quite a lot of work – using techniques similar to that used to check product quality. Of course, just like quality assurance itself it's hard work but achievable.

The biggest problem we see is companies who collect data from badly defined items with no proactive sample strategy to ensure the site is scored when it's busy and dangerous. These companies simply end up analysing pretty pie charts that give them misleading information on how safe the organisation is when it's nice and quiet. Worse, badly managed quotas for say "10 cards by the end of the month" might mean nine are made up in the van on the way home on the 30th To generate consistency you simply need to ensure that items are defined well.

Basically if you see a pie chart with "Inappropriate PPE" on it, it's worth asking "what do you mean by inappropriate exactly?" line managers should respond with something like:

"Well we have a map that shows where job-specific PPE should be worn and also a list of mandatory PPE. Boots should be worn at all times, so that's easy to score – but with splash overalls for example if the person is in a designated area we look to see that the overalls are:

- Done up to the neck;

- Sleeves rolled down and outside of gauntlet gloves (in case of splashing)

- Trousers outside of boots (ditto)

- Tears no greater than 2cm (so little nicks are allowed)

- Not overly impregnated with oily waste…

Now that last one is tricky to define, of course, so we have this borderline photograph that sets the standard … and worse than this (shows small encapsulated photo) and we fail them! The tricky bit is making sure we get out and score when it's busy … but we have a system where the supervisor covers me for half an hour while I do my observations if I need it."

If the supervisor responds something like that then he's part of a team collecting behavioural lead data that can tell you pretty accurately how much risk the workforce is running associated with inappropriate PPE use. You now know where the problems are and can measure how much better you're doing when you implement and analyse an action plan as detailed above.

Imagine trying to predict how likely we are to run someone over on a dockside. We can look at the near miss book, or at the training log for drivers and other employees (itself a lead measure according to the literature) but the best lead measure is to go out and observe the workplace.

- What percentage of drivers beep at blind corners?
- What percentage of vehicles are speeding?
- What percentage of pedestrians keep to the walkway?
- What percentage of pedestrians make eye contact with the driver of a van or mobile crane when in their vicinity?

Accurate answers to these questions will give you an accurate prediction of how likely an "undesirable, negative outcome, plant/ operative interaction" is!

The best lead measure. A really good example of measuring the quality of the process and not the outcome relates back to behavioural root-cause analysis. You can measure the gross number of suggestions put forward or of course the number of observations made. This can, of course, lead to lots of poor quality input – especially if there are rewards and punishments for hitting or missing quotas.

A good way to measure the effectiveness of an ASM system is to get a cross-section team together (workforce and management) who can agree whether or not the analysis has thrown up a 'high impact: low cost' suggestion – or maybe even a high impact but high cost selection. Of course the metrics aren't really easily tracked over time as a statistic at all – you'll start wanting somewhere between 'some' and 'lots' and if that goes well, end up after all the easy fruit has been picked wanting 'just a couple more'. But I'm sure you get the idea.

Summary of Main Points

- People who are given genuine choice and involvement are far more involved and committed to anything you want them to do.
- People often shift an attitude to match their behaviour, so if you can facilitate an improvement in safe behaviour – even if it's just one or two things – you've made a start.
- Lead measures predict the likelihood of an event.
- It's better to measure the process not the outcome.
- Measuring front line behaviour is the very best lead measure.
- Monitoring the quality of behavioural analysis is perhaps the best measure of the processes we advocate here.

CHAPTER 9

TYPICAL DIFFICULTIES WITH SAFETY LEADERSHIP PROCESSES

This chapter is about the difficulties in introducing an Affective Safety Management approach. As above, most companies understand that a key way of driving safety culture is for management and supervision to get out on the shop floor and exclusively look for and discuss safety issues. Again, the famous "count the basketball passes" clip is important here – when focused on day-to-day issues (or in this case basketball passes) we can miss really obvious and important issues – in this case a bloody great gorilla walking through the middle of the screen.

The previous chapters have covered contextual theory, made the case for introducing an ASM system and also covered some generic behaviours associated with a strong safety culture. This chapter summarises the research around this specific issue, covering the typical weaknesses that so often occur, and illustrates what best practice looks like. Many companies the world over have experienced similar problems when introducing such a system, so we might as well learn from them! Therefore the chapter is quite strategic in focus and is primarily aimed at individuals tasked with planning and coordinating an ASM approach.

A later chapter in this section then focuses on what we believe we can learn from the clever psychology of influence. As such, it is aimed at any practitioner or just any individual interested in increasing the influence of their communications at work or at home! I very much hope that the person mentioned above who is tasked with coordination and implementation will include it in any safety leadership training.

Problem One – A Lack of Planning

As the old saying goes "if you fail to plan … you plan to fail" and that's true of nearly all situations. So what planning are we asking for?

Check an ASM database or review previous safety contacts and consider:

- Who went on site last and what did they target?
- What did they find?
- What actions resulted? (And of course follow up on any actions and on how are things progressing?)
- Consider which jobs are being undertaken and when.

This will help ensure you don't turn up looking to target the same things as the last person. So for example you might note that no-one has targeted working at height for a while so you could look to target that.

You could of course find yourself waiting forever for it to be totally convenient to undertake a safety contact audit. However, please do show some discretion – if it's obvious the people you need to talk to are absolutely flat out, or if interrupting them could actually be dangerous, give them some space and look at something else for a while. Whilst you must of course make it clear you're not going to be totally fobbed off and leave, please do empathise. Simply ask yourself what would be reasonable if they were making an effort.

Problem Two – Lack of Depth

Please refer back to the chapter on root-cause analysis above, where the techniques are covered in detail. A summary overview is given here in case you're the sort of reader who has (quite reasonably!) skipped straight to the most practical section.

One of the biggest problems we see with systems like safety contact is that analysis lacks depth. We often get asked "how is it that things aren't getting any better despite the fact that we're put straight 1,001 things highlighted over the past year"? The answer is that often auditors will list any number of problems – but simply generate what's known as a 'crap list' of items that will recur.

James Reason uses a mosquito analogy. He suggests that if you have a problem with mosquitoes then a short term solution is to buy nets, repellent and swatters: a better solution is to find the swamp they come from and drain it. One of the causes of crap lists is that people can be wary of approaching someone they don't know – especially if they're uncertain of the technicalities of the job. So they avoid talking to them at all and just pick on something visible and easy like housekeeping – then pop an action point down around that. A hazard may well be removed as a consequence and that's always a good thing but it's really not best use of time.

Although we don't want to advocate anything like a formal 'follow these 7 steps' model here, if you cover the following four questions thoroughly will have a good discussion that may well generate some self-analysis in the person you're talking to.

The questions are:

- What does this job involve?
- What can go wrong?
- How do we make sure that doesn't happen?
- And, to repeat a key question from the previous section, "Is there anything slow, uncomfortable or inconvenient about that"?

Typically, as well as noticing the immediate risk once you've used your five whys analysis as above you may well find yourself considering such things as:

- Risk Assessments
- Barriers
- Signage
- Supervision
- Suitability of PPE
- Training
- Inductions
- Selection and Monitoring of Contractors
- Behaviours that are typical and not remarked on.

And so on and so on.

Working through such issues systematically and analytically – see notes on 'why' and ABC analysis above – and turning them into an action plan is a long way from a basic hazard spot. But doing these things systematically will nearly always require an in-depth conversation with the person doing the job. And that's where a dedicated open-minded safety contact comes in.

Problem Three – Getting Close Out ("Feedback Black Hole").

The first thing is to always be "SMART"!

Now we know that capital projects can be frustrating and time consuming to set up, and that we can all get so focused on the day-to-day realities that we're tempted to put the long term issues on the back burner. We've all been here... and the psychology of giving in to temptation was explained in the section above: in the short term it's a relief. However, we should not allow ourselves to be fobbed off with positive but vague and open-ended responses, and simply using our assertion techniques to ensure a SMART resolution is all that's required.

- Specific
- Measurable
- Agreed
- Realistic
- Time Set

Then just ensure this is followed up and that any support and resources required for completion are provided. Now it might be that a problem with a root-cause or contractor seems too big to tackle at a site level and this sort of local SMART resolution isn't really possible. In this case you may well need to make formal contact with senior management to articulate your concerns and observations. For those of you who are senior managers, please ensure you follow the same principles if someone comes to you with a concern – especially if you delegate the issue to someone else. It really wont be very encouraging for the ASM auditor if your response to a follow up call is "I asked Bob to look at it weeks ago … but I've heard nothing back yet." We all know they'll assume the worst.

Problem Four – "BS" merchants...

Now not all the people you interact with will fob you off with positive and vague language with the best of intentions. Some will just be trying to feed you a line of bullshit (BS) to get rid of you at all costs. You may well find this frustrating, if not positively annoying. Again I need to refer you back to the techniques covered above:

- Remaining analytical and "middle bubble"
- Using "broken record" technique to stop them wandering
- Keeping your language objective and behaviour based, explaining your reasoning
  – not personalising or generalizing

Let's see how that might work! Consider a scene between a hard working and long suffering supervisor – lets call him Andy – and an annoying and glib worker. We'll call him Rob. Andy approaches Rob in the car park:

Andy *"Rob, I noticed you didn't reverse park there this morning …"*

Rob *"You know I've forgotten again… I'll lose my head if it wasn't screwed on! I'll sort it later…"*

Andy *"Actually, can you sort it now ….and as it happens I've noticed you often forget … is there a reason for that?"*

Rob *"Well it's my neck isn't it? – I just find twisting so difficult since that accident in the gym"*

Andy *"Doesn't that make reversing out difficult too … Could you turn it around now please?"*

Rob *"Well I suppose it does make it difficult … but I do always check and do my best … "dib dob!"… do you know the wife's always leaving stuff on the back window sill … can't see anyway… wives eh? I'd get rid of her if I could afford it… coffee?"*

Andy *"Rob, will you please stop ignoring me and changing the subject…"*

Rob *"Andy I'd not dare ignore you! I've seen you on the five a side pitch... wouldn't want to get the wrong side of you ..eh?... eh? ... you watching the match Saturday?"*

Andy (Jumping up, pointing and gesticulating wildly) *"Get out there now and turn that car about, you idiot before I staple your head to the desk... You really, really piss me off...you muppet!"*

Now this would work perhaps but the person on the receiving end will resent you and probably try and get you back some time later – if only by dragging their feet. So let's try that again... this time without the inevitable consequences that follow leaving your "middle bubble"...

Andy *"Rob will you please stop ignoring me..."*

but instead of blowing up takes a very deep breath and with passion and gravitas says...

"Rob, I need you to turn the car around now. If you don't lead by example, you can't expect anyone else here to follow suit can you? Then visitors and contractors will take their lead from you all and soon the whole thing will be back like it was before ... and then someone will get flattened by someone rushing off home ... and this discussion will come to light and you'll look terrible as if you didn't care and I'll look weak... ...so can I ask you one final time ...could you turn the car around now please..."

The person really should respond to this. If they don't please feel free to shout at them as above or even sack them! After all life is short...

Problem Five – Quantity not Quality

A final problem is where people feel they have to spend a certain amount of time doing a safety contact. But it is quality we are after – not just going through the motions – so the good news is, when it's finished it's finished and there's no need to drag it out. If that's quicker than expected, fine – everyone will be happy. As we've said above, the key thing is to get out and about as frequently as planned and focus exclusively on safety at key times and in a motivated manner.

Conclusion

It was reassuring when we researched this chapter how much agreement there was with the "what goes wrong list". The typical comment was "that pretty much covers it!" I hope you feel the same comment applies to the attempt to address, in practical terms, what we can do about it.

Summary of Main Points

I hope you'll agree that applying the basic principles of ASM cover this list and I'd like to paraphrase them rather than just list the five points above again. That is:

- Ask the right questions
- At the right time
- Of the right people
- In the right way

Then you're plugged back into action; plan; do; monitor; review... and so on.

CHAPTER 10

COACHING SKILLS

I'd now like to start to cover some simple techniques that maximise the chance of you influencing someone to behave the way you'd like them to. The chapter first briefly covers the basics of coaching and then offers tips, techniques and golden rules of basic communication and interpersonal interaction. The next chapter provides tips on influencing someone to do something specific. When should you coach? When should you not? The simple answer to 'when should you coach?' is whenever and wherever you can! However, there are times when coaching may not be sufficient and it's simpler to list them:

- When someone is clearly an imminent risk to themselves or others, you will not want to be subtle and a "John, stop that now!" is appropriate

- When one or both of you hasn't the time and/ or it's a simple behaviour and a straightforward reminder is sufficient. (For example "John, the handrail please")

- When you discussed the issue recently – especially if you used a coaching style - and a simple "John!" (looking at the handrail) will suffice.

Coaching – The "Feedback Fish"

There are any number of detailed tomes and concise user-friendly books on coaching, and this section merely seeks to boil down the main techniques so that they can be set in context. (It's worth noting that some consultants run "behavioural safety" initiatives exclusively through safety coaching).

Feedback Fish. If you understand the feedback fish you understand the basics of coaching. Imagine your four-year-old has brought you a picture of a fish – but it's not very good, being only an outline. Instinctively you wouldn't say "that's rubbish that!"; instead, you'll say "oh that's fantastic. I'm so grateful you made the effort to draw me a fish! Thanks!" But then because you want them to improve you'll ask "I wonder? how could we make this picture even better? Let me think? How do fish see?" and your child will shout "An eye! We need an eye!..." and add one in, and similarly with swimming and fins, and so on ...

Many people worry that questioning technique will lead to people not valuing the process or feeling patronised, but studies show that just isn't the case and that people will use expressions like "it just came to me" or "when you think about it it's the only logical choice".

An example. We have a great team building exercise that can only be solved with a pulley system that has to be set up by someone throwing a ball wrapped in string around a table leg off a wall. There are times when the 'brainstorming' and 'problem solving in teams' is going badly and we want them to succeed of course so a clue is required. This involves the trainer acting like Steve McQueen's 'cooler king' Hiltz in the Great Escape and playing catch ball against the wall … but maybe only one time in 10 does someone say in the de-brief "well yes we solved the problem but only after you basically told us the solution!"

The key point is simple. You need to be positive rather than critical, whenever you can and ideally you need to get them to come up with answers themselves by asking the right questions rather than telling them the answers. It's coaching from you but it feels like discovered learning to them, and discovered learning (i.e. "oh I see!") is the best learning.

Communication

A footballer berates a referee and says "ref what happens if I call you a useless idiot?" The referee replies "I'll send you off!". The player asks "well what if I think you're a useless idiot?" The ref replies "you're free to think what you like". So the player walks away saying "Ok… I think you're a useless idiot!"

This chapter is about what is said and how it's said.

Of course all companies communicate about safety but its how well and how often that makes the difference. As the old joke goes – having sex badly once a month doesn't make you a great lover! Naturally, all behavioural models will stress that good communications involve high levels of praise and "catching people doing something right" is the expression used by the famous "one minute manager". (The effective use of praise is covered below under coaching). However, it also includes well delivered and high impact weekly briefs and tool box talks as well as an expectation in the workforce that communications on their part will be taken seriously and acted upon – not just filed in a draw. To help achieve this many companies have started to train all managers and supervisors in presentation, active listening, feedback and coaching skills. Bill McFarlan's book "Drop the Pink Elephant" (Capstone) covers much of this ground in a very accessible and practical way.

Perhaps the single biggest problem we see with organisations that are failing to be affective is that they have never addressed the communication or feedback skills of perhaps the most important people in the organisation – the front line supervision! Another interesting finding is the frequency with which supervisors attending courses of this ilk genuinely ask "my manager is going to go on this too aren't they? … only quite frankly he/she needs it just as much as I do."

Some high-level communication and influencing skills are covered in the another section, but I'd like to cover the basics here. Now there are short and long courses, numerous excellent DVDs and books that cover this material in depth. However, the basics are included here for the reader to be able to undertake a mental gap analysis. If you find yourself thinking that none of our managers and supervisors would know any of this stuff then …

Summary of Main Points

• Coaching styles that are appropriate and in context work best

• Always be positive rather than critical

• The effective use of praise is a key skill

CHAPTER 11

PRESENTATION SKILLS

I went into the audience and ushered a young lad on stage at an event I was running and asked him to "confirm these lines are genuinely parallel" (from the audience they look wavy – I was demonstrating some examples of Human Error). I'd picked on him as I'd noticed he seemed attentive and positive – smiling and nodding as I jabbered on. He just looked at me so I gave him his instructions again in a very clear and non-threatening way (well stage fright is a terrible thing), but once again he just looked at me. I asked him where he was from ... he just looked at me. Then to the lifelong delight of my co-presenter Ian Whittingham (the incomparable safety campaigner) I heard the shout "he can't speak English mate, he's from Poland!

Why he was in the audience at all is a moot point of course ... but someone felt he needed the message Ian and I were delivering on the day – and I checked after and of course he'd signed off his attendance when the clipboard went around. How many presentations have been made to people who didn't understand the message? The message Ian and I were trying to get across was important enough but it wasn't critical on the day. However, tool box talks and safety briefs often do contain information that may be required to keep you alive, but many are given by someone who mumbles or who renders the audience half comatose with death by power-point. They ask one question only... the closed "you all ok with that?" From the way it's said and the voice tone used even my Polish friend would fully understand that a nod is all that is required here and everyone can 'crack on'. Although this is not the place or even the right medium for advice on formal presentation skills, I would still like to suggest some basics. If someone in your organisation who gives important briefings can't meaningfully describe how they apply the following principles you may want to fill that skills gap as soon as possible.

Presentation Basics

Anyone can get to seven out of 10 as a presenter if they follow the following tips. If they do, then they get over the "useless" threshold and the audience will at least have to choose to disengage and not listen.

Getting it Ready

Prepare. You'll have heard the expression "If you fail to plan ..." and the following questions help.

- Who are the audience?
- What have they seen before?

- What do they need to take away from this?
- What are the politics around this? (What heckles and suspicions can I expect?)

A good rule of thumb is that if you can't talk naturally about a bullet point for a minute or more then you haven't prepared enough.

Top and Tail It and Logical Structure. Second, ensure that the meat of the thing has a logical structure. Something like "the problem, the options, the proposal" for example. Make sure this is surrounded by a news at ten top and tail. That is, you tell them what you're going to say, say it, then sum up what you've said. Most TV commercials and news bulletins work using this method to make them more effective.

Conclusion. Always ensure that the conclusion is a summing up of the main points – and never ever introduce anything new! (As well as being confusing the audience will always hate you for it. The end was close and you snatched it away!)

Graphics. First yes please! Pictures are always better than bullet points but props and graphics should be there for the benefit of the audience not the presenter. If it doesn't illustrate a relationship or show how something works etc, it should not be there. If you've ever heard a presenter say "now you wont be able make much sense of that at the back ... or from the front for that matter," then it is just a prop! They should go on to say "but it's my favourite slide and I'm not standing up here without it!"

Delivering It

Be Natural. Studies show that some people are more afraid of presenting than they are of dying – literally! But if you've prepared well, you're half way there because if you can talk you can present. You just need to prepare properly and take a deep breath!

Being able to talk naturally for about one minute per bullet point (or picture) means you are far more likely to be natural in delivery style – allowing your arms to wave about and the pitch of your voice to rise and fall. This is far more easy on the eye and the ear and user friendly than someone who drones on. It's just not as bad as you think it is! An inexperienced presenter will often feel horrible: everyone is looking at them; they're all alone; and they feel as if they will be judged so that when they walk in the pub or supermarket later that week the people there will shout "useless" at them. But in truth the people in the audience will, if they see you out and about, think "I know them from somewhere don't I ... now where did we meet?" remember that audiences generally want a speaker to succeed and empathise with their predicament.

So take a deep breath and remind yourself that, as you look at the audience, most of its members are more likely to be thinking about football or sex or shopping … and that if you can be concise and avoid being deathly dull they'll be very grateful.

Confirming Understanding and Getting a Discussion Going. You do this best by asking open-ended questions, ie. questions that don't have a yes no answer but are about what the person thought. You can't stop someone shouting "not a lot!" to the question "what do you think about that?" but it does lead naturally to the follow up "ok, but why not?"

Dealing With Heckles. First, if you've prepared well and thought about your audience you'll be prepared for the obvious ones. Second, the simplest technique is to acknowledge that you've heard the point made without necessarily admitting its right. Something like:

> *"so basically you think I'm just a suit who knows nothing of the day-to-day realities of actually working here?"*

This doesn't admit that it's true but merely acknowledging the point often satisfies.

Dealing with Genuinely Difficult Questions

The best bit of advice is don't waffle or give them some bull. If you don't know, say you don't know and don't try and waffle your way out of it. It never works anyway does it? Simply say "I don't know but I'll find out by Tuesday (or whenever) and come and tell you". (Of course, ideally, this wont be bull either!)

Ice-Breaking

Here are four quick tips on icebreaking to consider. First, don't make the classic mistake. Second, apply the magic of the word 'because'. Third, take a lesson from con-men and slick salespeople and fourth, the best questions to ask to get people talking.

1 Introduce Yourself and Explain What You're Doing…

A classic mistake people make is to fail to introduce themselves and explain what they are doing and why. I went to a nephew's school concert once when he was in his first year and all the parents in the audience were new to the school. At the end a woman popped up and started to wax lyrical about how wonderful everything had been and how impressed she was personally… and a chap who'd had perhaps had a drink too many before arriving mumbled far too loudly "and who the *&^% are you exactly?"… which was a bit unnecessary of course but pretty well articulated what everyone else was thinking!

2 Explain Why You're Doing It - the Power of "Because"

Studies show that people who explain why they are doing / asking for something are much more influential. Studies have shown that the word "because" is sufficiently powerful to persuade people to step aside in a photocopy queue by saying "please can I cut in here because I need to make some copies!" (The compliance figure in the study was 94% though you'll note that no explanation is given and what else would they be doing with a photocopy machine?).

Obviously, in the real world you'll be wanting to follow up the magic 'because' word with a sound logical explanation – if only because the study also showed it only works with relatively simple and straightforward things.

3 Building Rapport

People tend to like people who have something in common with them. They will, for example, be more likely to donate to a disaster fund for a town or country with a similar name. Studies show we rate people far more positively if they share some of their name – even if we don't consciously notice this. For example, research has found that someone called Dennis is almost twice as likely to end up a dentist as someone called George and someone called George twice as likely to be a Geophysicist. Of course if you found a dentist called Dennis and asked him if he'd been influenced in his choice of career by his name he'd say no and consider you crazy – but something is going on! (Really, statistically there should be about 260 dentists in the US called Dennis but there are around 480).

Salesmen and con men use this principle all the time when they desperately seek to find some common ground – or just make it up. Basically, nine time out of 10 if someone says something like:

> "You come from Cwmbran? Well I never my Uncle Ernie came from there ... lovely bloke he is ... my favourite Uncle!"

They are after your money.

Of course at this point everyone is all smiles – but they aren't smiling for the same reason you are! You could, however, more positively use this technique to build rapport before a safety discussion. The important thing is to not take it too far ... just find out some common ground and then leave it at that. In the above example the salesman might go on to say:

> "He always said anyone from Cwmbran is tough – but fair and can always spot a bargain!"

And the penny drops and all rapport is lost!

Advanced Rapport Building

I'm not suggesting you try and use this – just watch out for it!

More advanced techniques of rapport building include body language and language 'mirroring'. Mirroring – where people subconsciously copy or mirror someone's behaviour – is something that happens quite naturally when people are in tune so you can imagine you will naturally feel a sense of 'connection' with that person who is mirroring with you. (I say with you as you'll be doing it too). Many salespeople have been trained in this and try and mirror the customer so they feel they are 'understood' and listened too. So for example, you say "I could see myself in this car" then lean back, and a salesperson might well reply "you could see yourself in this car couldn't you!?" then lean back too. As in this example they'll also try and match your choice of sense – so if you 'feel' good they feel good. If it 'sounds' good to you it'll sound good to them too.

As above, most good salespeople have been trained in this … but watch out for it because again studies show mirroring works – unless it's done badly in which case you'll be deeply cynical (if you notice) or at the very least think they're rather weird! If you do notice, have some fun picking up and putting down pens and cups and the like, scratching your nose or standing down and sitting up. You can also use this technique more positively to check that things are going as well as you hope they are.

Whilst we are on the subject another way to have fun with salespeople is to watch out for one who asks you a question with only one logical answer – they are trying to 'funnel' you and it's probably one of a series of questions that are intended to take you to the last one which is of course 'so I'll get this wrapped then!". Instead, just give an illogical answer and watch for their expression! For example, the answer to the question "if I could show you a way of making this house cleaner for your children to live in and you could afford it – you'd be interested wouldn't you?". Just say "no, not really, over clean houses actually suppress the immune system don't they?" Or some such! Their next comment or question was firmly based on the assumption you'd say "yes!" There may well be a pause…

That said I need to make it clear that I'm not suggesting a good psychologist is always a match for a good salesperson. A natural born salesperson is already a master of the arts of psychology and usually pretty ruthless to boot!

4 Getting Them Talking

It's best to ask questions that are open ended rather than closed and also to ask feeling questions about what people think. Open-ended questions are ones that don't have a yes or no answer but instead ask such questions as "what do you think?", "can you explain?" or "how do you feel about that?" On the other hand if you ask a classic closed question such as "any problems?" you may well get a "no!" response just to get rid of you – even if that isn't a true answer. Consider the time you've been approached by someone with a clipboard. Typically we try to get around them if we can but if we do stop and talk we often find ourselves saying things like "and another thing!" or "write this down too!" and they are the ones trying to get away.

Two truths about human nature that explain why this sort of thing happens: first, no-one likes to be interrupted but second, we all seem to like being asked what we think more than we dislike being interrupted!

Summary of Main Points

- In an "Affective" company everyone who has to deliver a formal safety message verbally needs to be skilled in the basics of presenting.

- These are: plan it well; make the material user-friendly for the audience; and deliver it naturally not by rote.

- When presenting always introduce yourself and explain what you're doing and why.

- Use open-ended questions to get your "audience" talking.

- Try and make a connection with a bit of "rapport building" psychology.

CHAPTER 12

LISTENING SKILLS

A key skill in any sort of analysis is the ability to listen actively. Some of your colleagues of course could do with remembering to listen at all – let alone actively! I don't know about you but I'm pretty certain I myself could do to remember the old chestnut:

"We have two eyes, two ears – but just the one mouth. Work that ratio!"

Active listening is really all about paraphrasing and whilst there are all sorts of rules about listening skills the main one perhaps is to ensure you've heard the person correctly you reflect back what they've said – not just parroting it back but putting it into your own words and including the *feeling* as well as the literal meaning.

A famous example from the world of theatre illustrates the point. An actor was visited backstage by Noel Coward, who was prepared to be nice but not actually lie! Noel flounced in and announced "darling, you were sensational ... it was quite unforgettable what you did out there!". The actor asked "oh, so you liked it?" to which Noel replied "now, I didn't say *that*..."

When seeking clarification a good form of words to use here is something like "so what you're saying to me is...." This is important because many people will use vague language when it suits them to be misunderstood but saying yes to a question like that is a straight lie if it's not true. Of course some people will still wriggle at this point if it suits and not simply reply honestly "yes you're correct" or "no, actually you're not quite correct there". If this happens you need to turn the paraphrase into a "yes or no?" question.

Jeremy Paxman demonstrated this listening skill when talking to Michael Howard. Limiting an answer to either yes or no, in boxing terms, cuts the ring down on your opponent. Jeremy Paxman kept asking the former Minister "yes or no? ... you either did or you didn't threaten him so - yes or no?" The scene was played to much amusement on "Have I Got News For You" and after Howard's sixth or seventh deliberately obtuse and waffly answer they cut back to Angus Deayton, the compare, who nailed the point that I'm trying to make by observing "I think we can safely take that as a yes then!"

Imagine a manager who insists "no corners should be cut, but this needs doing by Friday at the latest!" The person on the end of this might reply "well I can try..." and then be more direct and say "I just can't promise to achieve both boss." At this point it will suit the boss to walk off having effectively delegated the problem – and of course leaving themselves all sorts of scope for manoeuvre if things go wrong – but a good response would be to ask: "I need to clarify this here. I can promise to get it done by Friday but I may have to cut a few corners? Is that acceptable? Yes or no?"

At this point the boss has to commit himself one way or the other – or refuse to answer a direct question. As Michael Howard found, refusing to answer has consequences too.

Assertion

Being assertive doesn't mean asserting yourself – it means of backing down but without getting aggressive. Of course, not being aggressive comes easily if you're analysing, rather than abusing, in the first place – but sometimes this analysis is not enough and there are all sorts of assertion techniques you can use. Again, as with presentation skills the following notes just cover the basics. That said, always adhering to these simple rules would make you one of the most assertive people in the country!

Saying Yes and No

In his "Pink Elephant" book Bill McFarlan tells a story of buying a coffee in the US and being offered a piece of pie by the waitress… "It's delicious, I baked it myself just this very morning etc". He didn't like to say no so 10 minutes later he and his colleague found themselves $10 lighter and about a thousand calories worse off as they saw another diner come in and receive the same 'irresistible' sales pitch. His response "no thanks, just the coffee is fine".

So, say yes when you mean yes and no when you mean no.

Don't Personalise and Don't Generalise

It is important to keep all language objective and impersonal – especially when you have to criticise someone. Never personalise or generalise – but stick objectively to facts about specific behaviour. You can describe emotion, but you can't show it. Imagine you see a worker not wearing a hard hat. Obviously shouting "Oi, you really do my head in! Get your hard hat on *nooowwww*" is all wrong! Instead, you should say something like "excuse me, I really need to talk to you about your lack of PPE. I'm really concerned about the risk you're running and to be honest I'm really not at all happy to see this … you've had so much training recently"

In the first scenario, the person on the receiving end isn't thinking about their risk - they're thinking about you and they'll be talking about you over coffee later as you've given them a perfect excuse not to focus on the risk they were running.

Criticism in Private

I remember a delegate once being unnecessarily rude to a waitress on a training course in front of his training manager. After a brief pause his manager politely and calmly asked him if could have a quiet word outside. There was no shouting but they came back in a few minutes later with the young trainee looking rather white and very chastened. The manager had ensured he'd had the maximum impact on him and (as a side effect) maximum impact on us too. I was sitting there really impressed with how the manager handled it. So impressed I can still remember his name now all these years later – Dave F. Giving someone a rocket in front of others may well increase its impact on the day but it will cause resentment and the best you'll get from the outcome is compliance through fear. Always criticise people in private.

The acronym RIPPIP is a good guide. Reprimand in private, praise in public.

Broken Record

Broken record technique is basically the same technique as TV reporter Jeremy Paxman used during that famous interview with Michael Howard as discussed above. What he did was he simply asked the same question again and again. The technique is to simply not move on until the question is answered. Clever people will of course try and drag you onto a new subject but you just hold your ground ... and repeat.

And repeat.

Challenge Waffle

You may just meet people on your travels that waffle and use vague language. Expressions like "hopefully!" and "as soon as I can" will be as bountiful as their smiles and good humour. You may find they smile less when you ask "can you be more specific please?"

Try asking a taxi controller "by 'just a minute or two' do you mean between 60 and 120 seconds; some time in the next five to 10 minutes depending on traffic but no later than 10 because the job is genuinely booked and someone is on their way – or you're doing you're best but in truth haven't a clue?" You'll be amazed how often they respond honestly!

When You're in the Wrong

– "Regret, Reason, Remedy"

As we discussed above when you're in the wrong you could try waffling … as it always works doesn't it? Or you could try the Basil Fawlty technique of pretending to pass out. Or you can try "regret, reason, remedy". Basically you simply say "I'm sorry, this it what happened and why and this is what I'm going to do about it". It isn't great to have to use it of course … but it minimises negative impact. Indeed, sometimes you can even improve things with it. There is a famous marketing fable about the pizza company that developed a great reputation by spending a month withholding every 50th pizza until one minute after the "if not there within 30 minutes it's free" promise. The delivery people were asked to wait until the 31st minute. Knock on the door and say:

- We're really sorry this is late!

- The new chef set the ovens just a bit too high and burnt your first one a little … not too bad but we didn't want to take the risk.

- So this one's free… enjoy!

This area touches on a basic principle that underpins Neuro Linguistic Programming and other positive thinking theories mentioned in an earlier chapter. It just isn't possible to live in a world where nothing goes wrong and everyone is perfect. It's how you deal with the various things that happen that counts. Following this rule makes you look more in control and credible than a typical waffle with the intended message "so as you can see, basically, this wasn't my fault" but which gives the unintended one "unlike the wise man who learns from the mistakes of others I don't even learn from my own mistakes".

"Bubbles!" – An Overview of Assertion

The 'bubbles' concept summarises the whole approach and takes advantage of the fact that we can't think and react instinctively at the same time. It has its basis in work in Transactional Analysis Interpersonal theory – which came out of California in the 1960s. I know that may set alarm bells ringing but it is actually all good stuff. The basic model is like a snowman with three bubbles on top of each other. The lower bubble represents passive, sulking behaviour. The top bubble represents aggressive, authoritarian or patronising behaviour. The middle bubble however, is where you ought to be – firm, fair, analytical and reasonable. You'll find that when you stop, step back and analyse yourself you'll be amazed how often you don't qualify for middle bubble status.

Some examples:

Consider first the manager who closes a meeting with a challenging "so we're all agreed? (rhetorical body language and voice tone!) any one got a problem with that? No? Good!" We all know that when things go wrong this person isn't going to say "well it was all my decision, given my voice tone and body language and the way I didn't give anyone time to respond anyway ... I effectively made it impossible for anyone to object didn't I?"

The theory also talks of the "nurturing parent" – still top bubble but without the aggression. The trouble is the side effects are that your paternal attitude may be seen as patronising (because it is – you're talking down to people). This mindset will inhibit other people's development and growth and will get in the way of your listening and communication skills as you're assuming you know best and we've already seen that a strong culture is based on listening and learning.

Have you ever said to someone "can I give you some advice?" How many said "yes please!" and how many either said "no – you can bugger off!" or, if they listened at all, did so grudgingly even when the advice was on the mark!

Why "Bubbles" Works.

There are two key factors to consider. First, thinking and reacting are mutually exclusive, so if you can train yourself to stop and think which bubble you are in .... you'll be half way there already. The second thing is to remember that behaviour breeds behaviour ... so if you're in your middle bubble other people will tend to match that. Sometimes it takes a little while of course but it will happen more often than not. On the flip side if you're not in your middle bubble it's really not very easy for people around you to be in theirs because behaviour breeds behaviour ... aggressive responses generate aggression or sulking but pleasant objective responses usually generate similar ones.

The real problem is that not being in the middle bubble always leads to problems later -and I do mean always. Being passive means you avoid confrontation but also means people will take advantage, you'll lose respect and you won't like the view in the mirror at the end of the day. Being aggressive means you might get what you want in the short term, but people will resent you and get you back in some way later.

I ran a course in Romania for a shipping company once where we discussed how this might work and the flip chart filled with such comments as "withholding information" "not helping new starts", "boycotting social events", "working slowly", "looking to leave the company", "slagging off the company in the pub" and so on. Then one young female pointed to a scar on her ear and said "or losing your head ... and I mean that literally!"

Her story was that a few months before she'd been examining a valve that had blown off and nearly taken her head with it – cutting her ear as it went. Basically, someone they never were able to catch had sabotaged it. It turned out there was a lot of bad feeling on board the vessel because of an "over the top" verbal 'rollocking' that had been dished out to the whole crew a few days before the incident.

Summary of Main Points

- It's vital to check the meaning of something as well as the details – the majority of a message is in the voice tone and body language.

- Use paraphrasing and yes/ no questions to close down the ring on people who are using vague language .

- Say what you mean and mean what you say. Problems don't go away just because they are avoided.

- Not being assertive always backfires in the long run.

- You can describe emotion but you can't show it.

- Say yes when you mean yes and no when you mean no.

- Criticise in private, praise in public.

- Use broken record and paraphrasing techniques to stop waffle.

- If you get in your "middle bubble" and stay there, every technique in this book will come naturally to you.

CHAPTER 13

TOP TIPS FOR INFLUENCING COLLEAGUES

Ever since Dale Carnegie, there has been all sorts of advice and guidance on how to influence people at work. Recent works such as Cialdini's "Yes!" have been added to 'classics' like the "One Minute Manager" and "The 7 Habits of Highly Effective People". The previous chapter covered some generic basic skills that, if applied will automatically help employees influence people as it will, of course, make them more effective in general. This chapter is an attempt to summarise the research that is of most use to people working "hands on" in the world of safety when they are after something specific...

If you've ever wondered why a dubious politician whose views you can't stand often sounds so persuasive – it's frequently these type of techniques they're using.

1. Praise!

The first technique addresses the thorny issue of "I know the theory about praise but how do I get praise into a conversation without coming over as an insincere creep and embarrassing myself?" One of the golden rules of a one minute manager is to "catch someone doing something right" and a key theme linking the "7 habits of highly effective people" is using praise to build people up. Studies show that praise is several times more likely to change a person's behaviour than criticism... Consider this example:

> *A manager takes a worker to one side and says "I know it's several months to your next appraisal – but I just wanted you to know I'm looking forward to doing it. It's clear you really took on board the points we made last year ... and we have noticed. Well done!".*

Would that motivate the person on the receiving end to pop out of bed with a spring in their step for the coming months? Well you'd certainly expect so... but consider how much criticism you'd have to give to match that praise. You'd have to go around to their house and shout at them every morning over breakfast! So whilst we can all appreciate the truth in this 'use praise' principle acting on it may prove a different thing entirely and most of us find giving out praise quite difficult.

Some tips on doing it well...

1.1 Praise and the "Top and Tail" Technique

We discussed this briefly under presentation skills but it works really well as a technique for praising too if the communication isn't entirely positive. The trouble with giving someone praise when they know full well a criticism is coming up is that they stop listening and in their head they are saying "yes, yes... all very good... but get on with and get to the bad news!" However, if you give them a summary of the message you can then go back and take your time with the positive stuff. This would sound something like:

> *"Andy, I need to talk to you about the report you did last week. Overall it was excellent, I particularly liked the way you set out the recommendations. Some of it was quite inspired. Some bits in the middle need some work mind and I need to talk to you about the graphs in particular – I thought they were quite weak actually but I've some better examples to show you. But overall, as I said, excellent well done!*

Now you can get into the detailed discussion...

1.2 Praise and Motivational Interviewing

This clever technique has its origins in work with delinquent youths of all things! It's a really good way of getting some praise into the conversation naturally and developing rapport.

The technique is to ask the person to rate themselves on a scale of 10 and you'll probably get back an answer "about seven I guess". Now whilst we want them to be a nine and the files say they should be a 10 the key here is not to ask "you what?! why aren't you a 10?" with the follow up "do you want to die?" but to ask "why not a zero?"... and then listen to the explanation. This will allow you to murmur, nod and generally be positive and praising quite naturally. It facilitates the development of rapport and allows their defences to drop a bit.

Then the follow-up question is "what would you need to do to consider yourself a 10?" and the following discussion may well involve some analysis and action planning that is meaningful to the person you're talking to. Let's consider how that might work with our friends Rob and Andy again:

Andy *"How would you score yourself as a driver? On a 1 to 10 scale..."*

Rob *"About a 7"*

Andy *"Why not a 1?"*

Rob *"Well, I don't speed much. Always drive the horizon not the car in front and leave my two second gap, I make that 4 seconds in bad weather and when I'm behind lorries and can't see".*

Andy *"I'm impressed ... you've done some defensive driver training...?"*

Rob *"No I just picked some things up from reading about it and so on..."*

Andy *"Good for you ... but you know what I have to ask next don't you... how can we get you up from a 7?"*

Rob *"Well in truth I do speed sometimes ... and I use the hands free too often... I know it's not illegal but I've seen the studies ..."*

Andy *"Why is that? Why do you speed and use the phone?"*

Rob *"Well it's usually when I get late and disorganised ... I get myself in situations where I kind of have to..."*

Andy *"Maybe you should try some time management ... I've got a cracking book about that in the car. Quite short, easy to read, lots of good tips. Would you care to borrow it?"*

Hopefully you'll agree that there is a good likelihood the answer to this will be yes and that "Rob" will actually go on to read the book and try and implement some suggestions. You should also see that the key question here is "why aren't you a zero?" because it ensures the chat starts with the discussion of some positive behaviour.

I kept away from educational psychology when I was training as it looked too much like very hard work! Picking up where this short section came in ... here's a genuine example.

"Johnny, how would you rate yourself as a student on a ten scale?"

"One maybe"

"Good... excellent.... Excellent! We can build on that!"

And bloody good luck to the dedicated psychologists who have those conversations on a daily basis.

1.3 Praise and "Positive Labelling"

A variation on the use of praise is its use when labelling a person. Studies have shown that people respond to positive labels well. An example would be where someone is interviewed about whether they are going to vote in an upcoming election and asked to pick a favourite colour or some such. They are told "it's interesting but people that pick that colour (regardless of what they said!) are far more likely to make use of their vote in an election..." and it is found that comment does indeed make the person more likely to vote in the upcoming election... Imagine a football coach talking to a striker who has missed a few chances recently. They can see he is on the cusp of losing confidence because in the last match he passed a few when really he should have shot. They might say something like this:

"do you know, one of the things I like about you is that you never lose confidence when you miss a few ... you keep going ... I can almost see you thinking 'the law of averages must kick in soon ... I just need to keep going and keep my head up...' Do you know it's a great example to set to the younger players of how to deal with missing a few chances".

We can obviously use this in the world of safety by saying something like "it's a good job you always wear X or don't take Y shortcut because with your level of experience people around here will look to you for their lead ... and will follow your good example".

1.4 Praise to "Get You On Your Way"

Research has shown that if you tell people they get something for free if they "save eight tokens" they are approximately half as motivated than if told they need ten tokens but 'here's two free to get you started'. In the latter situation although eight tokens are still needed "you've made a start!" and are twice as likely to start 'collecting' tokens!

In light of this research, it's worth asking which manager is most motivating. The manager who points out that a worker isn't wearing his correct PPE (gloves missing) or the one who praises the wearing of hat, boots, reflective vest and goggles and who says "if you were wearing your gloves too you'd be perfect!".

1.5 US Consultants, ABC Theory and Praise

In the US especially, some senior consultants suggest that the way to get a soon, certain and positive reward into the situation is to use praise. (Please see chapter five on the vital importance of consequences of behaviour under root-cause analysis.) This is fine as infrequent praise works so it doesn't have to be very time consuming and, as we've said, well delivered praise works everywhere and not just on some ever smiling 'good old boy' from Oregan who thinks Ireland is the capital of Scotland.

However, often this seems to be the primary focus or what they advocate – with the objective analysis of root causes given less emphasis. So it's worth stating that I personally believe a behavioural model that effectively uses praise alone is missing the key element of a good behavioural approach and may be guilty of giving too much emphasis to the individual as discussed in chapter four.

2. Admitting that You're Not Perfect is a Strength

– And An Opportunity

Studies show that people have been shown to trust people who admit they don't "know it all" – and that the moment when you are most persuasive is just after you've admitted you don't know it all – and they've decided you might be someone they can trust.

So don't go in all guns blazing with the big things you want agreement on, instead hold back and wait until the moment's right. Don't say "I want this!" and then "but now we're talking, as it happens, I don't know about this, so please tell me".

Make sure you do it the other way about: "I don't know about this so please tell me..." and only then "I want this!"

3. Never EVER Suggest Something Risky is Typical

Social norms have been shown to be even more important than was recently thought. So it's important never ever to suggest that the individual is part of a bigger problem and that lots of others are guilty too. We all like to think we're individuals but research shows clearly that we look to the behaviour of others much more than we say we do when asked.

Saying "everyone does it" hardly ever generates the thought "oh, that's terrible!" but means instead that it's normal and as we've already seen in previous chapters normal is very often taken to mean it's basically OK. Studies show that the closer to home the reference group the more powerful this effect is. So if you could get away with it an ideal thing to say would be something like "no-one else who works here now or ever before has ever done this unsafely". Of course we're not suggesting you lie like that – just trying to illustrate the point!

Further, there will be key individuals wherever you are that are looked to more than others. You'll know who they are of course and time spent getting them on side is time really well spent. There is a chapter in Malcolm Gladwell's influential book "The Tipping Point" all about the vital importance of key people in generating change. He calls them Mavens, Salesmen and Connectors.

Ideally of course you'll use these techniques rather than bribes and threats!

4. Make it 'Personal"

There's a safety campaign in Australia that has the line: "If you drink and drive you're a bloody idiot" and often in the US you'll see a sign near some road works that says "please slow down, my daddy works here". Most people know instinctively these are effective and I'll try and explain the reason here.

First, imagine you're booking a table at a nice restaurant. Consider these two typical conversations:

The person booking the table *"A table for two, Saturday at 8pm please."*

Reservations *"That's all booked for you … please ring if you can't make it."*

Diner *"Yes, OK."*

Replay with a slightly different wording:

Person booking *"A table for two Saturday, at 8pm please."*

Reservations *"That's all booked for you … can I ask you will you please ring and let us know if you can't make it?"*

Diner *"Yes OK I will.".*

You may be surprised to know people are only a third as likely to fail to show up without ringing when asked the second way. It's because of the "will you" and "yes I will" in the conversation. Though similar words are used it's much more **personal**.

So what we're suggesting is that whatever you're asking for – and certainly when it's about safety – look people in the eye, mean what you say and ask "will you". Then make sure they look you in the eye back and give a personal commitment to act.

Further, everyone we work with has something they're passionate about. For many of us it's our children. For others it's a sport or a hobby … so it's obviously a good idea to also talk about these issues during a conversation about risk. You don't have to be so direct as to say something like "how would your son feel if you fell from here and paralysed yourself!?" Instead you can simply ask something like "so you enjoy a kick about with your son?" and let them join the dots.

5. Never go "Strong BUT Weak" – always "Weak BUT Strong"

Research has shown the order words are spoken in can impact on us subconsciously. (In a previous chapter covering management commitment we mentioned this briefly explaining how a manager can communicate their level of commitment without either they or the person they are talking to consciously knowing it).

The night before I wrote this chapter I was reading an interesting book by a famous Fleet

St. editor who is well known for being a bit on the "manipulative" side. He described a call with a reporter who was in Baghdad when the second Gulf War started who was a bit worried about his safety. Our man describes saying to this chap "if you want to come out just do it ... but ...you're doing some fantastic journalism in there".

This is an excellent example of the following principle - which is, never ever put anything important before a but in a sentence – as essentially a but means 'forget what I just said and focus on this next thing coming up'. So it's weak but strong... never strong but weak... Consider these two communications about a Safety action plan.

> "So I can't stress enough how vital it is that we get this list closed out by the end of the month ... but ... that said I do appreciate it's going to be difficult."

> "I do appreciate it's going to be difficult ... but... that said I can't stress enough how vital it is that we get this list closed out by the end of the month."

As I'm sure you can see the second version is far more powerful ... even though we've used exactly the same words.

What's interesting from a psychological point of view is that though the manager has effectively communicated his level of commitment to the operative neither know that it's happened as it's largely a sub conscious message.

6. Give People a Face-Saving "Out" If At All Possible

This tip is that if you back people into a corner they just get defensive – so always give them a face-saving out if you can. Some new information they probably didn't know about is always a good face saver. Consider this example of a safety manager trying to get a worker to hold the handrail.

Rob *"You need to hold the handrail! ... you could fall there."*

Andy *"Yeah alright...."*

Rob *"No, don't be like that. It's important."*

Andy *"Yeah, OK I heard you... "*

I'm suggesting that this works better:

Rob *"Can I ask you to hold the handrail?"*

Andy *"Yeah, alright."*

Rob *"I know it sounds a little thing but I've just seen some figures showing that slips trips and falls made up 40% of all accidents at our sites last year… and that cost us about half a million or so … staggering isn't it!"*

Andy *"Half a million quid! from slips trips and falls!"*

Rob *"I was the same when I first heard… amazing isn't it!"*

In the second example the person is far more likely to be open-minded to your request as they will be less likely to get all defensive.

7. We Don't Like "Loss"

Studies show clearly that people really don't like to lose things they already have – even if they don't seem to value them much. Sales of seats on Concorde went through the roof when it was announced it was to soon cease flying. Certainly perhaps the most powerful element of the personal testimonies by such presenters as Ian Whittingham, who was paralysed in an accident, and Ken Woodward, who was blinded, is that they are saying "look what I've lost" and "you could lose it too"

This does not negate anything said above about being positive and using praise rather than criticism when you're talking to someone about their safety. But it does make sense to talk about their good health now … and how easy it would be to lose it in an instant.

8. Be Nice

Finally, and especially if you don't really have much authority, another way of not backing people into a defensive corner is simply to ask them nicely to do whatever it is you'd like. Another hugely influential principle of society is that of reciprocity and fairness. Most of us just hate to feel in people's debt. Charities have picked up on this and send out free pens with begging letters in the hope you'll feel obligated to respond. In the case of being asked nicely we (usually!) feel some obligation to reciprocate and promise.

If it's a pleasant exchange they will, of course, be more likely to mean any promise to change their behaviour in the future. Again studies constantly show that the more a person means a promise they make at the time – the more likely they are to stick to their word later on when no-one's around. Does that sound like it might apply to a chat about PPE or some such?

Influencing Tips – Conclusion

Now obviously if you have the authority you can skip all this psychology stuff and just insist forcefully they do what you want them to do. Then you simply have to monitor them 24 hours a day, seven days a week – indefinitely. As we said in chapter three – if you treat people as adults they'll probably act in an adult way. I said most people probably. I know who you're thinking about but they're in a minority! Please don't you ignore all this good stuff just because what's his face is a total idiot!

Summary of Main Points

- A little praise really does go a long way!
- Not being an expert on everything actually makes you more influential.
- Describing anything as typical is also saying it's OK.
- Make sure any interaction is personal not impersonal!
- Never say anything important before a "but".
- Always try and give the person an 'out' so they don't get defensive.
- Being nice obligates people to respond positively in some way.

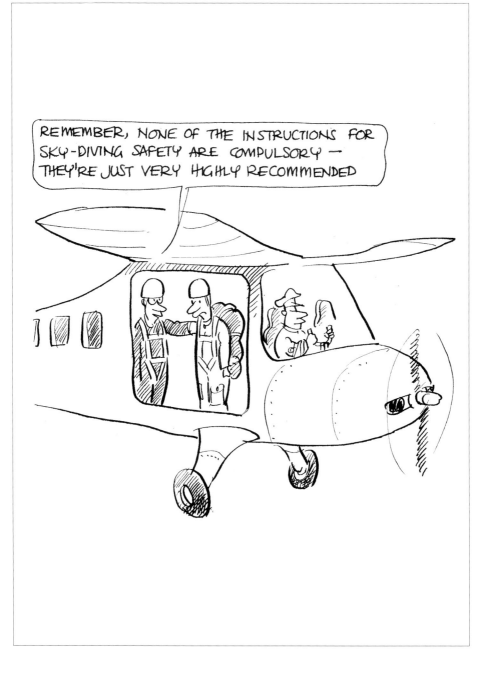

CHAPTER 14

SUGGESTED IMPLEMENTATION METHODOLOGIES

Before suggesting some alternative strategies it might be useful to give an overview of the basic model of ASM. The obvious first recommendation is simply to implement the following.

"Affective Safety" – An Overview of the Basic Model

• Plan a strategy whereby all management visit the shop floor at least once a week to concentrate exclusively on safety- or at the very least - to have safety as the first item on the agenda.

> • Ensure these visits are at the busiest time that is logistically feasible and safe. When undertaking ASM (and at other times).
>
> • Ensure you always model safe behaviour yourself.
>
> • Ensure you use praise whenever you can … if that's difficult for you then suggest they use the "rate yourself on a 10 scale" approach.
>
> • Ensure that after introducing yourself and asking "what are you doing?" the first open question is, "is there anything slow, uncomfortable or inconvenient about doing this job safely?" Or is it actually logistically impossible? (i.e can they do the job safely – even if they want to).
>
> • If there is a problem – or if you stopped to discuss an unsafe act or condition you saw – then they must analyse why it happens/ has happened and what can be done and come up with an improvement action if at all feasible.
>
> • Ensure you don't just tell them if you know something that they don't … coach them with such questions as "what do you think?".
>
> • If you need to get some sort of a promise from them – make sure you don't back them into a corner and get a grudging one. Aim to get one they give gladly …
>
> • And of course follow up with praise, progress feedback or monitoring as appropriate.

If all managers and supervisors regularly follow the above I assure you that your safety culture will be ' just', proactive and strong! Easily said, I know.

A Suggested Strategy

Although I am hoping the reader will be thinking "there is a lot of good stuff" here, I am aware that some will be asking themselves "but where do we start?" As well as implement an ASM approach as above I'll make some other suggestions about methodologies that can be applied with the above or as a stand alone. Every site and organisation is different and constantly changing. You'll know what's most appropriate at this time for your situation. The following are therefore some suggested strategies.

Enhancing what you already do

- First get all the in-house safety trainers – or the key ones at least – onto a "how to run a high impact" training session. There are good but relatively inexpensive generic versions available from the likes of P3 and Croner. Then re-vamp the training.

- Second, if they aren't already, ensure that all safety training objectives are tied in directly to any formal management appraisal process and given suitable weight.

- Follow this up by running some 360 degree feedback (i.e. asking the workforce) to find out how well you're doing.

Doing Something New (Management)

- Undertake a safety culture audit to identify where you are weak.

- Establish an Affective Safety Management process where all management commit to touring the worksite once a week, at least, to talk to the workforce about safety concerns. (And of course as above).

- Ensure they receive suitable training before they do this so that they are able to maximise impact, influence and analysis whilst minimising negative impact. (At the very least this means training them in Behavioural Root- Cause Analysis Skills and Coaching Skills).

Doing Something New (Workforce)

- Ask for volunteers to receive similar training to above so they have the chance to enhance their analysis and interpersonal skills.

- Ask them to identify a dozen key daily behaviours that could be improved. (From PPE to the quality of tool box talks).

- Ask for some to design and tailor a half day "sheep dip" for the whole workforce covering key theory as well as "what we need from you" and then get them to role it out themselves. (They may need some presentation skills training).

- Ask them to use their new skills to analyse the problem and come back to you with as many high impact, low cost solutions as they can. Validate these and implement any that are high impact and low cost as soon as possible. Also implement as many high impact but high cost solutions as logistics allow.

- Say thank you for their input publicly and sincerely.

A final case study

I was working with a chemical company in South Wales and we had run a full behavioural programme (see chapter five above) that had gone very well. All the easy wins had been achieved and we'd already had more than half the workforce volunteer to be trained as behavioural observers. All managers were trained in the skills as described above, modelled safety at all times (well, very well!) and challenged behaviour frequently and well. Near miss reporting was up too (always a good sign) and the latest lost time incident over a year ago.

So as well as rolling the process out to home and driving safety, the MD wanted to push on further in the factory. He said "We always have to push on! So what's the core of this then? – it's those ideas the guys came up we've put into action isn't it! We need some more of those". We discussed what people had received for contributing to date and how well giving out fire extinguishers for cars and other symbolic gifts had gone down. He suggested hard cash and we discussed how cash for safety isn't a very good idea usually … 'so many unintended side effects'. He replied "that's as maybe but this is a rewarding process not outcome really isn't it and if the buggers out there can bring me any more high impact low cost solutions I'll happily pay them cash myself!" I drove off feeling pleased with my work and looking forward to all the safety awards they would surely be winning.

Then the parent company closed the factory.

The financial realities and politics of organisations can be a real headache for consultants but all we have to do is give good advice and run training sessions that get high scores on the 'happy sheets'. Then we get to go home. I'm frequently in awe of the patience, dedication, doggedness and sheer professionalism of safety professionals and managers who have to deal with it day in and day out. I think one of the reasons I trained as a psychologist is that I'm not sure I could do the job without losing my sanity – or as we say back home in Wales 'frankly I'd go stark staring'.

A Final Anecdote

Some years ago I was at the Singapore safety conference and met a man who said he'd been everywhere, done every job and had seen it all. I asked him which country was the least safe in his opinion – expecting a 'third world' answer. Instead he said "New Zealand – they're all mad".

It reminded me of a visit I made to New Zealand many years back where I saw a sign by a small airfield saying "sky diving". I stopped and asked how much it was and how much training was required to go up. The instructor said: "Well we brief you thoroughly on the way up and off you go. So no time at all really". I said "bloody hell, that's a bit worrying to be honest … when I looked into it in the UK they insisted on a fair bit of training … what if I get it wrong, come over all panicky and forget what to do?"

The tough looking Kiwi just looked at me and said: "I bloody well wouldn't if I were you mate!"

So to finish this book as we started it with a favourite saying of the leading safety campaigner Ian Whittingham MBE.

When it comes down to it safety isn't complicated.

WORLD CLASS TRAINING

Over the years we've learned what world class training looks like from experience ,from books and by attending training events by acknowledged leaders in the field. (You'll not be surprised to hear that a lot of the innovations seem to take place in The City with financial training. If it's good enough for people chasing their next million it's good enough for safety). The following notes summarise this generic learning. You are, of course, invited to use the principles to underpin the specific chapter by chapter exercises described above.

1. Training Set Up

1.1 Location

Ideally, it will have a good amount of space – about 10sq m per person – natural light and a comfortably cool temperature. In addition, again, it will ideally have lots of colour on the walls – relevant posters etc. If you can't get delegates to a hotel or training centre then use something as close to this sort of atmosphere as you can.

No-one ever learned very much in a hot, noisy, cramped environment. In truth unless you are quite unashamedly seeking signatures in a file as part of a back covering exercise , is the cost benefit actually worth it?

1.2 Mindset

You don't need me to tell you that studies show that most delegates will remember only a handful of things from a course. Therefore getting these embedded is key and taking quite a while getting them in the right *mindset* to learn is fine. So it is best practice to relax them with as many ice-breakers as you feel you need. For example some leading trainers will suggest silly games with a very simple learning point, jokes and humour and of course round table introductions that might take a couple of hours to set up a two-day course!

Combining both – why not have some nice *music* playing as they walk in and throughout the day when appropriate. Something lively but without lyrics (or with simplistic lyrics) is ideal. After all if it's a mindset set up technique good enough for people trying to sell you sofas, biscuits and the like why not use it when it's something really important like safety?

1.3 The Learning Funnel

This means as well as spending a lot of time setting up the right mind set we should also spend time setting up the specific learning point. So for example you might be covering how listening skills are key to good safety communications. So you could set this up by:

- Introducing the general principle – i.e. that being a bad listener is a bad thing, maybe illustrating this principle with a clip from TV to make it memorable

- Make it organisational specific (ideally with an active session) – e.g. in groups discuss and describe good and bad listeners you know/ have worked for or with

- What does "good" look like in behavioural terms? What does "bad" look like? What were the consequences? And what they think of the individuals in question?!

- Individual training (some formal input about key listening skill techniques such as paraphrasing followed by an active role play and de-brief)

2. Delegate Energy

Imagine someone walks into a electronic goods shop and approaches a salesman. He says "I saw some interesting looking CD players in the window, some looked really good. Can you show me some please – I'd like to take a closer look. Imagine if the salesman is a music buff who instantly starts talking animatedly about speaker quality and the like and shows the potential customer a boring looking but excellent (sound) quality product. Now imagine if the salesman just shows the person a really sexy looking one with average but good enough sound quality.

The latter salesman wins hands down because he picked up on the fact that the customer is very visual. (The sentence repeated with the key words highlighted – "I saw some interesting looking CD players in the window, some looked really good. Can you show me some please – I'd like to take a closer look"). Some of us are visual, others aural (So 'I like the sound of that!') and others kinaesthetic (So 'I have a good feeling about this'). There's no need to get too hung up about all this but trainers do need to remember that different people are motivated by different styles of input – watching, listening or doing.

2.1 Learning Styles

It is always worth remembering, therefore, that different people have different learning styles. Some are strong verbally, others strong spatially. Some like visual input, some like to listen and assess other like to do things with their hands and try things out. Given that it's rarely feasible to tailor and re-write a course for each new intake good trainers make sure they rotate the input by, for example, using power-point slides, then short films then a hands-on exercise, then an exercise where delegates discuss these in groups and report back and repeat.

It is not patronising to suggest that the typical blue collar worker is more likely to prefer a practical and hands on learning style than a person in a business suit.

2.2 Movement

A bad way of getting delegates' views is to ask them when they are sitting at their tables "Are you all ok?" (The response is usually "yeah" or just "Ugghh"). A better way is to:

- get delegates in small groups to gather around a flip chart (starting with having to stand up and walk to it)
- discuss what they think
- stand up and report back.

The physical movement itself is energising. In addition considering their opinion is also much more active as a learning style. Again it raises energy.

2.3 (Really) Hands On

As mentioned above as well as "active" exercises many delegates will be used to working with their hands – and many will work in that environment because they like it and/or are very good at it. So when they are doing an exercise with scores for example (e.g. a simple personality test that tells you the answer to the question "are you a red, blue, yellow or green personality?") why not have them build a tower with Lego bricks of different colours of their answers rather than just paper and pencil?

As well as having something to do with their hands they can be very creative sometimes as they build and others can, of course, see their scores – which promotes more interaction and banter. This again promotes more energy.

2.4 Individual Exercises & Music

When your delegates are doing something relatively quietly – like completing a personality questionnaire this is, of course, a good time to put the music back on. Just like those builders next door who should have been finished months ago, most people like some music as they work. Again, you'll want something without lyrics – or with unobtrusive lyrics.

2.5 Make a Role Play Competitive

One exercise that adds energy to a room is to make a role play competitive. For example we have an assertion exercise where delegates practice their broken record / middle bubble technique. The idea is that a homeowner is trying to avoid paying for all four double glazed windows until the one of the four that broke as it went in is replaced. The fitter is trying to get all the money up front and leave with a vague promise to come back "as soon as possible" to fix the window.

The audience are primed to declare one or the other the "winner" by the following criterion. First if the home owner is dragged away from the broken record (Which is "I'll give you 3,000 now and the final 1,000 when you fix the broken one") he loses. (The "fitter" will ask such "don't you trust me?" or "how can I get the replacement window without the money?" and on one memorable occasion when he knew his colleague to be a born again Christian "I ask you as a Christian - what would Jesus do?"

The learning point is that the audience can see that if he starts to debate *anything* he's instantly in trouble because it becomes a battle of wits and resolve (So "it's not about whether I trust you … I'll give you 3,000 now… " keeps the owner in the game … anything else and it's clear control is being lost and they're out!).

The home owner 'wins' if the "fitter" really goes for it and throws everything at them and after a pregnant pause the home owner replies calmly … "I'll give you 3,000 now…" and the audience, knowing a lost cause when they see one instinctively laugh.

3. Close Out and Review

3.1 Review

The key learning points at the end of the day. Many companies are now using "concert reviews" which are reviews of the day's main points set to music and in front of relaxing scenes (waterfalls and mountains etc). As the material covered is very easy to watch but still relatively new, the delegates will be focused – but relaxed – as watching a film is not at all threatening or anxiety inducing. Focused but relaxed (for example finishing your crossword in a nice comfy chair with a coffee) is the ideal learning state.

Studies do show that learning is best when the person is challenged and stretched but in an environment where they can try out new skills with support and little fear of failure. This 'focus' is called 'flow state' – a state in which delegates are fully focused on the task or material and time passes quickly. It's easy to see the link with the points made above. Relaxed delegates undertaking lots of "buzzy" group exercises to try out new skills, followed by a concise de-brief, is ideal.

3.2 Team Quiz

If you haven't the technology for a concert review then a team quiz is also a very good way to review learning. (Though ideally, of course, you'll do this as well). Why not make it a physical exercise with chairs etc representing a "race track" where the team moves forward one chair per correct answer etc? Again, a little bit of healthy competition, mixed with physical movement and challenge is ideal for energy and ideal for memory and learning. Putting the delegates in teams of course makes it focusing but not too anxiety inducing.

4. Follow Up

It's said we haven't really learnt something until we have used it for real 30 times. (Really, think of driving a car on your own, a professional skill such as counseling or playing a sport. How long did it take until you felt you'd really mastered it? For example, how many times do you need to play golf before you stop saying "I'm learning to play golf" and say instead "I play golf" or how many people would you see before saying "I am a counsellor") This means in practice:

- keeping the number of things delegates need to do back in the workplace manageable
- following it up with reviews every few months
- tying it into their formal appraisal system if they have one – maybe even some form of formal mentoring and coaching

Informal mentoring and coaching is, of course, essential.

Finally – A Highly Recommended Exercise for Supervisors

This exercise builds on the behavioural theory covered above and the need to use active exercises to maximise the chance of 'discovered' (i.e. "light-bulb") learning. You'll have appreciated that much of what we have covered in this book stresses a certain black or white nature of safety culture. For example, that lack of always modelling safe acts is disastrous and that not challenging effectively means condoning.

The exercise works as below and can of course be done in two parts. Part one at the start of the course and part two at the end:

- Construct a 2 by 2 matrix on the floor with a sheet, rope or just chairs
- Show that one axis is "how important I am to safety leadership" and the other is "how good I am at leading safety"
- Ask them to walk into the grid and stand where they think they themselves are
- (Or where the company is/ typical supervisor in the company should be).

Most will stand in the middle – i.e. quite important (with a bias to not important we usually find) and quite good. Now stop the exercise.

- Train supervisors and/or managers in the key points of safety culture. (Or remind them)

- Ideally show a hard hitting video to focus them on the human cost of accidents (HSE's 'Turning Concern into Action'; 'Marion's Story' from Drive Smarter; 'Ken's Story' from Outtakes for example).

Take them back to the grid.

- Point out/ remind them that anyone with any authority – or even just some experience is a safety leader whether they like it or not. They cannot stand in the middle of the grid – that's just a fudge.

- Point out/ remind them that because of the way the 'little bit of risk is OK' mindset combines with Heinrich's triangle (and other key theory) they can't really be average at safety leadership. Basically, either they are an effective safety leader – and therefore part of the solution – or they are part of the problem.

- Ask them to stand where they think they are now.

- And where they'd like to be

You should now have some very thoughtful delegates. This exercise also works well with the CEO, MD and the rest of the board. First get them to accept the validity of the theories we've discussed – then ask them to stand where their typical supervisor should stand.

DRIVING SAFETY AND HOME SAFETY

The editors and I talked about this and agreed that this appendix is really too short to do such an important subject justice, and that this might not be the appropriate place to raise it. We also asked the question "if we do address driver safety why not other important issues like stress and back injuries?"

For what it's worth the behavioural and ergonomic issues addressed above pretty much cover the root causes of manual handling and posture issues. The material also covers stress to a greater degree than you might think as stress audits will find that you need to do two things to reduce stress. First, you need to change the terms and conditions of employment – so of course most companies move straight on to the second set of recommendations and these will relate to increasing the involvement of the workforce in decision making and communicating effectively and fairly with staff – that is that decisions are based on objective analysis. In addition, it will emphasise that managers need to develop their interpersonal skills and it's all about enhancing trust, fairness and clarity of communication. I hope you'll agree we've tried to cover all of that in this book.

However, we decided we would make an exception for driving safety as for most companies the biggest single cause of loss will be an area they don't even target at all. It's an activity that's on a par in terms of danger per minute with deep sea fishing and deep cast mining.

Of course many companies consider home safety generally to be important and this makes perfect economic sense. In most industries you are far more likely to lose someone to an accident at home that at work. Consider the impact on a company's bottom line following a weekend when:

- The financial director falls off a ladder washing windows (too mean to pay someone to do it for him probably)

- The chief engineer's daughter falls off an unguarded trampoline and paralyses herself

- The MD is involved in a head-on smash on an A road.

Some real case studies illustrate the opportunities here.

- At a recent safety event, the Head of Safety of a major transport company estimated their current cost of accidents as around £40M pa

- The Head of Safety of a major sales company had worked out that the cost of non standard service repairs to cars not even crashed – by which he meant upholstery damage, (overly) worn brakes and tyres, scratches and the like – to be some £12M pa

- Another company that had reduced its accident rate by 20% had been able to negotiate a £1M reduction in insurance premium

- Finally a major international company embarked on a hugely aggressive driving safely programme when it realised its last three fatalities worldwide were all managers driving to work. As well as on-line training for all and defensive driver training for many, they now insist everyone go through an assessed "commentary drive" every two years. This is best practice in our experience.

Finally, I'd like to mention a curious case study to illustrate the point that "driving is more dangerous than flying". Joanna Ganthaler was an Italian woman who famously missed checking in minutes too late for Air France 447 from Rio on the 1st of June 2009. The papers were full of stories about her along the lines of "talk about a lucky escape!" Two weeks later she was killed instantly in a head on car crash on an 'A' road in Austria. But then, for the majority of us, almost nothing we interact with is as dangerous as an A road.

Basic Strategy

Typically a Management of Occupational Road Risk Policy will look something like this:

- First, there should be a clear strategy and vision – from the very top – with clear responsibility, accountability and monitoring and review. Obviously, monitoring and follow up should be proactive, not reactive. There should be standard risk assessments for standard journeys and a system of dynamic risk assessments for new or unusual journeys. The very best policies will incorporate training and follow up of that with such processes as commentary drives for all employees

- Second, whenever reasonably practicable, road travel should be avoided or reduced through the use of video conferencing, home working and trains for example

- Third, it's vital that the individual has the right vehicle for the job, the right training to use that specific vehicle and of course all vehicles are in a safe condition

- Fourth, journeys should be planned safely, risk assessed as appropriate and contingency time built in. (In practice, setting off with sufficient time to obviate the need to speed and with time to stop for a coffee, a stretch and to retrieve the phone to check and respond to messages)

- Fifth, drivers should always drive defensively. If they can't be sent on defensive driver training then find some DVD modules that can be accessed remotely. (See for example DriveSmarter.com).

Two key principles

- Managers must lead by example. If senior managers don't reverse park for example, how can we expect others to follow? Managers cannot ever pretend they haven't noticed that a colleague has answered the phone when driving their car for example

- The second principle is that consultation is key! For example, when new technology can be implemented it is essential that the end user is consulted about the day-to-day practicalities – just in case some side effect causes as many accidents as the benefits prevent!

A 'design it out' case study

Some years ago I was driven across Romania to a seminar by a man who clearly had a death wish. The roads were poor, the cars fast and powerful and the local 'norms' quite terrifying. I overcame my embarrassment by thinking of my children and asked him to slow down. However, the fourth time he looked at me as if I was rather sad and timid I lost my resolve, gave up, tripled checked my seat belt and crossed my fingers.

I got there in one piece and so did the MD but he had a brief but alarming visit to a ditch on his journey. Apparently, even promising to cancel the contract only helped him a little. We discussed solutions and agreed there was just the one: next time we'd ask all delegates to congregate at Bucharest airport and we'd hire a charter plane and fly them the 300 kilometres to the conference location! A little more cost but a lot less risk.

What Can You Do?

Behavioural Safety. DVD packages and on-line material now exist that allows the principles and behaviours of defensive driver training to be cascaded to all of the workforce cheaply – or even outside of normal work hours. For example, if you adhere to the following behaviours you can drive on a motorway almost indefinitely without incident.

- Follow the two second rule as a minimum not as ideal and increase that to four seconds in bad weather

- Drive to the horizon not to the car in front so you can anticipate events

- If you come across an unexpected jam pull up 100 yards behind it and use your mirrors in case someone behind you isn't paying attention!

- You are already assuming everyone about you is drunk, stupid or both. You will also have planned your journey well enough to have set off in good time, have built in a contingency for delays so that you have time to stop and check messages and won't be tempted to speed.

These behaviours overlap with other areas such as Country Lane and A road driving where additional key behaviours are such as 'only overtake when you know you can do it safely not when you think you can'. In a road rage incident a key behaviour is to press the horn and refuse to make eye contact with the person who has just got out of their car. (Because the noise attracts attention, you can't be drawn into a macho and/or 'it's getting personal' confrontation and because you wont be able to hear what they are saying either!)

Obviously, these are just examples of key driving behaviours but you can see that the principles of behavioural safety apply just as well to driving safety as to any other form.

Coaching and Analysis. In the book we described techniques for coaching improvement and analysing problems that maximise analysis and impact and minimise defensiveness. (These being "what's inconvenient about keeping to safe behaviours?" and "how would you rate yourself on a ten scale" technique). Clearly, not only do these apply directly to driving safety they are also, for many, the only way a manager can hope to impact on the behaviour of colleagues driving behaviour whether it be at work or otherwise.

Peer-to-Peer Challenge. Imagine that you are in a colleague's car and you want to challenge their driving because it's worrying you. Obviously, using the techniques of assertion, communication and influence discussed in the book will maximise the chance of your colleague slowing down and not inviting you to walk the rest of the way!

Personal Risk Levels. These packages come complete with personality and risk assessment models that allow individuals to assess their specific level of risk. Working out that you are 100 times more likely to be killed driving to the supermarket than you are to buy a winning lottery ticket when you're there can concentrate the mind!

Driving Safely – Conclusion

Many companies have done very little about driving safely. Leaving aside the human cost, and given the costs and opportunities briefly detailed above, it's frankly very difficult to understand why.

RECOMMENDED BOOKS AND DOWNLOADABLE PAPERS

"Beyond behaviour"

M Anderson, Safety and Health Practitioner, March 2008. (Downloadable at rydermarsh. co.uk/ articles and case studies)

"Games People Play"

E Berne, Penguin (1964)

"The One Minute Manager"

K Blanchard and S Johnson, Harper Collins (1983)

"The 7 Habits of Highly Effective People"

S Covey, Franklin Covey, (2003)

"Only Human"

Health and Safety at Work. Dorrell, J (June 2009)

"The Tipping Point"

M Gladwell, Abacus (2002)

"Blink"

M Gladwell, Penguin (2005)

"YES! 50 Secrets from the Science of Persuasion"

Profile Books; NJ Goldstein; SJ Martin; RB Cialdini (2007)

"Emotional Intelligence"

D Goleman; Bloomsbury (1996)

"Strategies to Improve Safe Behaviour as part of H&S management system"

Keil Institute, Contract research report 430/ 2002"

"Leading health and safety at work"

HSE and Inst of Directors. (Downloadable at hse.gov.uk/leadership)

Leading Health and Safety at Work

HSE and Inst of Directors (Downloadable at hse.gov.uk/ leadership)

"Safety Management and Safety Culture: The Long, Hard and Winding Road"

In W. Pearse, C. Gallagher & L. Bluff (Eds.) *Occupational Health and Safety Management Systems*. Crowncontent, Melbourne, Australia. Hudson, P.T.W. (2001)

"Who Moved My Cheese"

S Johnson, Vermilion, (1998)

"Drop the Pink Elephant"

B. McFarlan; Capstone (2003)

"Brillaint NLP"

D Molden and P Hutchinson, Pearson, (2006)

"Managing the Risks of Organisational Accidents"

J Reason, Ashgate (1997)

"Leading Performance Indicators"

Step Change in Safety; (downloadable at stepchangeinsafety.net)

"The Wisdom of Crowds"

J Surowsiecki; Abacus (2004)

"Learning from Disaster – A Management Approach"

Toft, B and Reynolds, S Palgrave 2005

RECOMMENDED BOOKS AND DOWNLOADABLE PAPERS

"Organisation Choice"

in Organisation Behaviour and Human Performance Vroom, V (1966)

"Psychology at Work"

Warr, P.B. Penguin, (1987)